THE LOST GARDENS

Camellias
Rhododendrons

NATIONAL PLANT HERITAGE COLLECTION

In 1950, a group from the Royal Horticultural Society visited Heligan. Amongst the group was author Mrs Howard Spring. She records that the tenant, Commander Thomas, confided to her that because of the vast size of some of the rhododendrons, he expected - or hoped - that they would be given the status of national monuments.

This heart-felt hope was finally realized in May 2007 when Plant Heritage recognized not only Heligan's rhododendrons but also its old camellias as plants of historic importance, worthy of National Collection status.

This is the story of those plants: what they are, where they came from, how they came to be at Heligan, and the conservation programme that will ensure that they continue to enchant future generations.

BEE ROBSON

Acknowledgements

I thank Heligan Gardens Ltd, who contracted the research on which this book is based, for allowing me access to their image archive. I very much appreciate the contribution of all the Heligan staff who have helped to make writing this book not only possible, but a pleasure.

Published by Barman, Little Beside House, St. Day, Cornwall TR16 5PX
Copyright B A Robson 2010

ISBN 978-0-9564889-0-9

Design and typesetting by Mind's Eye Design
www.mindseyedesign.co.uk

Photograph credits
Julian Stephens © Heligan Gardens Ltd. Cover, prelims, Index, pages 4, 9, 10 photo 1, 26 photos 1 and 2, 32 photo 1, 34 photo 1, 38 photo 1, 39 photo 1, 40 photo 1, 50, 67, 68, 70 photo 1, 72 photo 1, 73 photos 1 and 4, 74 photos 3 and 4, 75 photo 2, 76 photos 1 and 3, 79 photos 1 and 3, 81 photo 3, 84 photo 1, 86 photos 1 and 2, 87 photos 1 and 2, 88 photos 1 and 3, 89 photo 3, 95.
David Hastilow © pages 28, 29 photo 1, 42 photo 2, 45 photo 3, 70 photo 2, 82 photos 2-5, 83 photos 1 and 2, 84 photo 2, 89 photo 1.
Ruth Perkins © Heligan Gardens Ltd. Cover, prelims, Index, pages 75 photo 1, 79 photo 2.
Ros Smith © pages 90 photo 1, 92 photos 1 and 2, 93 photo 3.
Sarah de Courcy © Heligan Gardens Ltd page 93 photos 1 and 2.
Mike Friend © Heligan Gardens Ltd page 88 photo 2.
Jonathon Jones © page 13.

I am indebted to all those who have allowed me to use their photographs, especially Julian Stephens whose pictures have made such an important contribution to this book.

All other photographs by Bee Robson.

Photographs of the squires are reproduced by courtesy of Tremayne archive: photographs © David Hastilow.

Pictures of old rhododendrons from *Rhododendrons of the Sikkim Himalayas* by Joseph Hooker are reproduced by courtesy of Tremayne archive: photographs © David Hastilow.

George Edward's Chinese Pheasant is reproduced by courtesy of National Museums Scotland 000-000-606-892-R © National Museums Scotland. Licensor www.scran.ac.uk

The picture from Samuel Curtis's *Monograph on the Genus Camellia* is from the 1965 Charles Traylen facsimile of the original edition of 1819.

T-Kishikawa
Pictures of camellias from Chandler & Booth catalogue 1831 entitled *Illustrations and Descriptions of the plants which compose the natural order Camellieæ, and of the varieties of Camellia Japonica, cultivated in the gardens of Great Britain*, from Abbé Berlèse's *Iconographie du Genre Camellias* and from the Verschaffelt catalogues *Nouvelle Iconographie des Camellias* are reproduced by kind permission of T-Kishikawa © who made these invaluable plates from the original books and to whom I am very grateful for his generosity in allowing me to use his images.

The maps were created by Ruth Perkins © Heligan Gardens Ltd.

M – always and forever

Contents

1
THE STORY OF A VICTORIAN GARDEN

Heligan House is in Cornwall, in the parish of St Ewe, five miles from St Austell. It stands at the head of a deep valley that runs down to the sea at Pentewan, a mile and a half away. For four hundred years the house was the home of the Tremayne family. It is rather a secret house. It cannot be seen from any road, or even lane, only a distant glimpse from a few clusters of houses down on the coast. It stands, surrounded by its own land; its long sloping lawns, its deep wooded valley to the south, its pleasure gardens to the north: the whole almost encircled by tree-lined rides.

The house itself was never famous. It is large and impressive rather than of great architectural merit. It was a family home, a private house and, although now divided into apartments, it still is.

It is the gardens that are renowned and the story of the gardens has its beginnings in the story of the Tremayne family itself, how they came to be in possession of their estate and how the house as we see it today came to be built.

THE FOUNDING OF HELIGAN

The story of the Tremaynes is the story of a family who, over the course of many generations, acquired and accumulated land and wealth. Originally there were branches of the Tremayne family in both Devon and Cornwall, and it was a Devon Tremayne, Sampson, that bought Heligan in 1536.

A STRATEGIC MARRIAGE

Sampson died in 1593, leaving the property to his son William, who had already established his intention to make Cornwall his home by marrying a local girl from Lanzearth, Ann Pye. The Tremayne family was beginning to show a marked skill in strategic marriages.

In 1603, when James VI of Scotland was making his way down south to inherit the English throne from Elizabeth I, William Tremayne built himself a hall house, a style very much in fashion in the late Elizabethan times. The estate passed to William's son John who continued the process of aggrandizement by marrying into the wealthy Dart family from Pentewan. The family fortunes were in the ascendant.

A COUNTY DIVIDED

The English Civil War brought a reversal in the family fortunes. England was divided: Cornwall was divided: the Tremaynes were for the king. John Tremayne's son Lewis sought a career in the army where he rose to the rank of Colonel in the King's Foot Regiment, a position that he held when the war broke out in 1642.

CORNWALL AT WAR

In 1645, after early successes, the Royalist cause in Cornwall was losing strength. Lewis Tremayne had retreated to Pendennis Castle in Falmouth. Pendennis Castle and St. Mawes Castle on the opposite headland guard the entrance to the Carrick Roads, the navigable waterway that leads deep inland. Here he was besieged; his opposition to the Roundheads almost costing his father the loss of his estates. The Tremayne fortunes were at a very low ebb.

All their sufferings were not in vain. Charles Stewart returned from exile in 1660 and, generous to those whose loyalty enabled him to regain his throne, he made Lewis Lieutenant-Governor of St. Mawes Castle.

THE WILLIAM AND MARY HOUSE

By the time of Lewis's death in 1684, the family was becoming both wealthy and prestigious. The estate passed to his son John. It was valued at £1662 4s 4d, a lot of money when you consider that a working man would only earn about £30 per year.

Professionally, John was successful. He rose to become Sergeant-at-Law to the joint occupant of the English throne, the Dutchman William III. He became knighted, wealthy and required an establishment which would reflect his social position.

During Sir John's frequent and prolonged absences attending Court in London, the estate was run by his mother, Mary Tremayne and it was Mary who, in 1692, undertook the site management of the rebuilding programme. The house was redesigned in the ordered and restrained style favoured by William and Mary. It was to be made of brick, a material rarely used in Cornwall because it was believed that bricks crumbled in the wet climate. Dedicated to following fashion, John brought his own brick maker, Richard Burgess, to Cornwall, instructing him to produce 300,000 bricks at 5/- per thousand, the bricks to be made at Heligan's own brickworks.

There is no record of the location of the brickworks but there are, close to the gardens, small deposits of a bright orange clay that closely matches the colour of the bricks used for the wall of the Poultry Court. John had then to find a bricklayer, not easy in Cornwall, and it was George Chetwell from Morwenstow in Devon who got the job. Mary kept detailed records of the work and it is in these records that the garden is first mentioned, redesigned to reflect the French style of formal courts and paved terraces.

The main building work was completed by February 1693 but Sir John had little time to enjoy his splendid house; he died the following year.

A HOUSE WITH CAPABILITIES

The development of the house and gardens continued into the Georgian period.

The elegant stables and clock tower were built in 1735 and the gardens were redesigned by John Wade. His plan shows a formal and intricate design consisting of twelve areas separated by walks and probably edged with box.

John Wade's garden was short-lived. It was already an anachronism. Ideas were moving quickly on. This was the age of William Brown, who was said always to have assured new clients that their site had "capabilities". The landscape style of garden design was in vogue and it was in this period, in 1766, that Heligan passed into the hands of Henry Hawkins Tremayne.

FORTUNE'S FAVOURITE

Henry was both lucky and astute. Destined for the Church, he unexpectedly inherited on the death of his elder brother Lewis. He married in 1767, an auspicious marriage to Harriet Hearle of Penryn. Their pre-nuptial settlement gives an idea of the extent of their estates. Harriet's dowry included £6000 in public funds and property in twenty-nine parishes. Henry, in addition to Heligan and other land at St Ewe, owned property in twenty-four Cornish parishes and ten in Devon. Henry spent the next sixty-three years consolidating and expanding his patrimony, to become one of the leading landowners in the West Country.

It seems he was most fortunate in his wife. Loveday Sarah Gregor wrote of him:

(He was) *"most deeply attached to his wife and fully aware of her superior talents... I have always looked on Mrs Tremayne as a pattern to wives who are united to men of less ability than themselves. So invariably respectful was her tone in speaking of her kind partner, so cleverly did she guide him as the speaker of every sensible remark, the author of every wise resolution, that she established for him a character far beyond his merit...."*

Henry Hawkins Tremayne

Fortune continued to smile. In 1784, when he was forty-three, he inherited the estate and mansion of Croan from his cousin Dameris. The Sydenham estate of the Devon Tremaynes also fell into his hands as did the estate of Rashleigh Barton and, on his own account, he bought land and property in the area surrounding Heligan.

From being comfortable, the Tremaynes of Heligan had become rich. Henry had plans to improve and upgrade his house as befitted his station in life. He started to rebuild in 1810 and by 1824 Heligan House was considered to be a splendid mansion.

PARADISE PURSUED

Henry spent the later years of his life creating the ideal country gentleman's estate suited to the gracious living and social intercourse of one of the county's leading families. He had built himself an impressive house and when he came to consider how his gardens might complement his fine house, he took their redesign very seriously.

This was the era of the landscape style and its greatest advocate, Capability Brown, was moving, if not heaven, certainly earth and very large amounts of it (not to mention entire villages), to achieve the required vistas and the impression of informal and natural beauty; a landscape of muted shades of green, of undulating lawns and rolling parkland, whose distances were accentuated by clumps of well-placed trees. Henry was inspired by the work of landscape designers to transform the gardens at Heligan.

Garden designers were no longer the prerogative of royalty and the aristocracy. Their skills were in great demand and the cleverest of them even entered into the literature of the day. In Jane Austen's *Mansfield Park*, published in 1814, Humphrey Repton is spoken of as the most appropriate person to advise on the improvement of a house and grounds:

> *"Your best friend on such an occasion, said Miss Bertram calmly, would be Mr Repton, I imagine."*

His fee is mentioned: five guineas a day, an enormous sum for that time.

Humphrey Repton did some work in Cornwall. Most famously, he designed the gardens at Anthony House, but he is also known to have worked both at Caerhays and at Tregothnan. Henry Hawkins may well have seen the results of his work on the estates of his near neighbours.

MR GREY, LANDSCAPE GARDENER

Humphrey Repton may not have worked at Heligan, but it seems his ideas had their adherents in the St Austell area. One of these was a Mr Grey. Sir John Colman Rashleigh tells us about him:

> *"Mr Grey, the landscape gardener, came to Prideaux (House, Padstow), November 20th 1812 and gave me some valuable hints, but he was a strict and bigoted pupil of the modern school, that which the famous Capability Brown founded and ..... after him Repton adopted."*

The Rashleighs were related to the Tremaynes. Henry's sister Grace had married Charles Rashleigh of Menabilly, and in spite of his relative's poor opinion of him, it was Thomas Grey that Henry commissioned to redesign the inner estate.

Thomas Grey produced a design which he entitled *A plan of Intended Alterations for Hilligan the Seate of the Rev Mr. Tremayne*. For the first time, the gardens begin to look recognisable. There is shelterbelt planting around the Northern Gardens, a double row of trees lines each side of the Eastern and Western Rides and along Beacon Path. The Melon Yard is there, together with some small structures or pits inside, and there is a rather vague outline of what will become the Flower Garden. The large walled garden to the south of the house has been removed and the planting in the valley now much more closely resembles the shape of the Jungle as it is today:

> *"The whole of the grounds ... are rendered delightful by the natural unevenness; deep valleys, where the rays of the sun scarcely penetrate, watered by purling brooks, and enlivened by cascades, the surfaces of which are covered with lively plantations, adorned with temples, and rendered easy in ascent by a variety of walks that wind over the shady precipices, and afford agreeable resting places at every convenient distance"*.
>
> (W Peneluna An Historical Survey of the County of Cornwall Vol 1 1838)

GRACIOUS LIVING

Heligan was almost self-sufficient. All meats, poultry and game were produced on the estate, and fish was landed only a few miles away. Grain for bread, apples for cider and hops for beer were all to hand but by the beginning of the 19th century this was not enough. Head Gardeners were required to broaden their scope of knowledge and extend their skills to encompass the growing of the new fruit and vegetables now arriving in the UK.

SEASONS IN THE SUN

Henry and his family led an elegant social life. His sister Grace's diaries describe their engagements and the entries show that they entertained widely. Anyone lucky enough to live down in Cornwall will know how popular they become from Easter onwards! The country house season was well-established: for the duration of the parliamentary summer recess, friends and relations would gather at country estates, away from the heat of the capital, and it was the job of the head gardener to produce sufficient vegetables, salad crops and fruit, all concentrated within these twelve weeks. Added to this there was another dimension: competition. Henry and Harriet would no doubt have vied with their neighbours in offering their guests unusual or out-of-season produce and there was significant prestige attached to the growing of such delicacies as citrus fruits, peaches, nectarines and especially pineapples.

The Pineapple Pit at Heligan is based on a design that was published about 1822 but the fine detail may well have been the result of the Head Gardener's expertise and ingenuity. It was heated by the fermentation of farmyard manure and it must have taken a great deal of trial and error to manage the system successfully. Henry Hawkins died an old man in 1829: it is hoped he lived long enough to taste his first pineapple.

A PERFECT SETTING

Henry's legacy was a balanced and pleasing design, suited to the needs of the family both in terms of produce and pleasure. The paths enclosing the gently sloping pleasure grounds were sufficiently extensive to give the ladies of the house daily exercise whilst the more energetic could take the rides down through the valley and round the outer estate.

In the pleasure grounds a network of underground pipes had been installed, both for drainage and irrigation, powered by Heligan's first ram pump and, in the many corners of the globe where England had established her interests, men were gathering the plants that would bring this garden to life.

The story of the development of the gardens from this point is the story of the three garden-makers: John Hearle Tremayne, squire from 1829 to 1851: his son, John, squire from 1851 to 1901, followed by his son, John Claude (Jack) squire from 1901 until 1949 but who left the estate in 1923.

Their stories are told in the living plants that make up the gardens at Heligan.

Heligan House

2

THE FOUNDERS OF THE COLLECTION

History comes very close at Heligan. The faithfully-restored buildings ripen the pineapples, grapes and peaches just as they did 150 years ago. The Vegetable Garden, still worked by hand, produces varieties of fruit and vegetables that the Victorians would have recognised. These working gardens and structures are often regarded as the heart of the gardens, but if they are the heart, the life-blood is the plants, encircling the pleasure gardens to the north and flowing down the steep valley of the Jungle.

From the rich and diverse accumulation of plants, two genera were chosen to become special features, camellias and rhododendrons and it is these two groups that are the subject of Heligan's Plant Heritage Collection.

All three squires were passionate plantsmen, and during their respective periods they introduced the finest of the new plants that were coming into England from all over the world.

John Hearle Tremayne

The 19th century was the greatest period of expansion in the history of this country. Political and commercial exploration brought new markets within reach, as well as the raw materials needed for industrial development. Plant-hunting was entering a new phase: alongside the passion for collecting botanical rarities was exploration for commercial plants, not just for food and raw materials but to satisfy the ever-growing demands of the nursery trade.

John Hearle loved trees. A busy man, he served Cornwall as an MP for twenty-five years but found time to indulge his passion. He was responsible for much of the early tree-planting at Heligan. He began with native trees: the great oaks, beeches, limes and yews, many of which still survive.

It was the exotic trees, however, which really stirred his gardening blood. He had a fine stage on which to display his much-prized acquisitions. He planted *Podocarpus totara* introduced from New Zealand in 1842. He planted *Araucaria araucana*, each seed costing 2 shillings, a day's pay for a gardener and the modern equivalent of approximately £60. He planted the hard-won *Pseudotsuga menziesii* or Douglas Fir that David Douglas sent back in 1827, seven years before his horrific death.

All of these trees John Hearle planted in the area now called the Jungle. They are still there. You can look down the valley and see them, not just as trees but as living monuments to the lives of courageous men.

John Hearle is responsible for the beginnings of the Collection. Camellias were new to England and the earliest camellias at Heligan were likely to have been planted by him, but it is to the rhododendron Collection that he made his most significant contribution, not by planting but by marrying Caroline Matilda Lemon, sister of Sir Charles who was a friend and sponsor of the great plant-hunter, Joseph Hooker.

John Hearle died in 1851. His son John inherited not only the estate but his father's love of camellias and he planted many of the new varieties being raised on the Continent.

He was fortunate enough to reap the benefits of his father's advantageous marriage and, through his uncle Sir Charles Lemon, received seeds from Joseph Hooker's remarkable expedition to India. During his time, the bulk of the rhododendron Collection was planted, both original species and the later hybrids, some of which John may have raised himself.

John Tremayne

John Claude Tremayne

The last of the squires of Heligan was John Claude, Jack as he was known. He designed the pretty Italian Garden; he planted the lovely *Davidia involucrata*, many different species of bamboo and contributed to the ongoing development of the gardens by planting some of the new rhododendron introductions from China, together with many of the beautiful hybrids that were being raised in Cornwall.

It was the passion and foresight of these men that the created Heligan's magnificent Collection of camellias and rhododendrons.

Chronologically the camellias came first.

3
TEA AND CAMELLIAS

CAMELLIAS IN HISTORY

Camellias are deep within the culture both of China and Japan. Oil from *Camellia oleifera* was used for dressing the hair. Camellia oil was, and still is, highly valued for cooking, having a high smoking temperature and being low in transfats.

The wood of the camellia was reputed to have magical powers that were effective in driving away evil spirits and promoting healing: the large and colourful flowers of the japonica species were part of religious ceremonies and are still used today.

In Japan camellias, especially the higo camellia, became associated with the samurai culture. The sight of a blood-red camellia dropping from the tree, the whole of its bloom intact, symbolised the death of a samurai warrior in the flower of youth, decapitated by a sword.

A PLANT THAT CHANGED THE WORLD

Mention camellias and, for most of us, the image that comes to mind is of the spring-flowering shrub. Many people would be surprised to know that they are familiar with one type of camellia plant in a way that they had not realized, the plant called *Camellia sinensis*. T'Chai, the mandarin word for this camellia, is commemorated in the now old-fashioned expression – a cup of cha! In other words, tea.

THE STORY OF TEA

Tea has been drunk in China for almost 5000 years. Legend has it that in 2737 BC Emperor Shen Nong was travelling, visiting one of his provinces. Whilst resting beneath a tree by the side of the road after a heavy meal, his servant was boiling water for him to drink. As luck would have it some leaves from a nearby tree blew into the open pan. The emperor, curious, sampled this brownish liquid and felt instantly refreshed.

Tea became one of the seven basic ingredients of Chinese life, together with fuel, rice, oil, salt, soy and vinegar. There are many stories alluding to the stimulating properties of tea. In 460, the founder of Zen Buddhism, Bodhidharma, was born in Madras. In the course of his studies he travelled to China where he undertook a seven-year sleepless vigil. Hardly surprisingly, after five years his eyelids began to droop and, incensed at this display of weakness, he snatched them off and flung them to the ground where they sprouted into two camellia bushes. Bodhidharma found that by chewing the leaves, he was able to finish his vigil.

The tea camellia, *Camellia sinensis*, has small single flowers, a pale creamy yellow in colour, insignificant by comparison with the more showy blooms of the japonicas. The virtue was in its leaves, which were plucked, semi-fermented and then dried.

Camellia sinensis at the Tregothnan estate in Cornwall

TEA BEGINS TO TRAVEL

In 805 seeds of *Camellia sinensis* were introduced to Japan. It took another three hundred years, and the introduction of Zen Buddhism into Japan in the 12th century, for tea-drinking to become an integral part of the cultural and spiritual life of Japan.

Religion brought tea-drinking to Western Europe. Father Jasper de Cruz, a Jesuit priest working in China, had brought his tea-drinking habit back to Portugal by 1560 and, by 1610, the Dutch had begun regular shipments of loose tea into the Netherlands. Some people in Europe, botanists and entrepreneurs, were beginning to realize the importance of tea as a commercial crop and Europe wanted its own live plants.

The great Swedish botanist Linnaeus had visions of establishing tea plantations in Sweden and encouraged travellers to obtain tea plants for him from China by any means, fair or foul. The journey was long and arduous, the plants did not survive and the seeds turned rancid before they reached Europe.

There is a story reported in Curtis's *Botanical Magazine (vol vi 3148)* that, even after almost 200 years, still has the power to elicit our sympathy. It is said that one ship had finally managed to reach the harbour of Gottenberg with a single plant still in good health. The captain, anxious to show his prize, placed the plant on the table in his cabin and left it there overnight. In the morning he discovered that it had been eaten by rats! Linnaeus gave the sensible advice to sow seeds in pots on departure from China so that they could germinate on voyage. Following this advice, young tea plants arrived at Gottenberg on 3rd October 1763 and were taken to the Botanic Gardens of Uppsala, but conditions in Northern Europe were unsuitable for tea production and the plants never become more than an horticultural curiosity. Recently, however, the Tregothnan estate has succeeded where Linnaeus failed and has a thriving tea plantation.

In the 17th century, trade took tea to Eastern Europe: it reached Russia over land, travelling in the caravans of Chinese traders along the Silk Road through Samarkand and Bukhara. Journeys could take as long as a year and, to survive the rigours of a long sojourn in the saddlebag of a camel, the fragile tea leaves were compressed into hard bricks. When the traveller wanted to drink, he would use a knife to shave off fragments of the dried leaves into boiling water.

THE FASHIONABLE DRINK

Tea quickly became a fashionable drink in Europe: England was slower to adopt the habit but here politics was about to take a hand.

Charles II was restored to the throne of England in 1660. There was much rejoicing by the majority of the English people who found Cromwell's Puritanism not to their taste, and great relief for Charles himself who was heartily sick of enduring an impecunious existence as the unwelcome guest of the French court. In 1662 he married Catherine of Braganza, daughter of King John IV of Portugal. Catherine brought with her Goa, Bombay and a chest of tea. She was much addicted to tea-drinking: her first request when she landed on English soil was for a cup of tea but so scarce was that beverage in England at the time, there was none available. That was quickly to change: her taste for tea created a fashion at court that was soon adopted by fashionable society.

From the royal court and the salons of the elite, tea-drinking spread to other sections of society and was embraced with the greatest enthusiasm. The impact of tea and coffee on the drinking habits of the nation is explained, at least in part, by comparison with what had been available hitherto. There was water, of course, but too often the water in the cities was unsafe. Milk was readily available and was wholesome when not adulterated with chalk and alum but it had a very short shelf life. Alcohol in its various guises and strengths was probably the safest in terms of intestinal health but now, suddenly, there was a drink that tasted interesting, that did not intoxicate, was acceptable at the highest level of society, and incredibly, made you feel so much better.

This was the effect of caffeine, so powerful a stimulant that extravagant claims were made. Tea was advertised as a panacea for apoplexy, catarrh, colic, consumption, drowsiness, epilepsy, gallstones, lethargy, migraine, paralysis and vertigo. It also had its detractors: William Cobbett was one. He said that it *"destroys health, causes effeminacy, leads men to idleness and women to the brothel"*, and claimed that there was *"undeniable proof: tea kills pigs"*!

For the most part, however, the medicinal benefits were praised, both by tea importers and medical men alike although their opinion was not always to be trusted: one medical man was as convinced of the efficacious use of tea as he was in the benefits of rubbing hemlock on young ladies' frontal orbs to produce an improvement in their health!

TEA GOES PUBLIC

The new beverages began to be sold in public. Both tea and coffee were soon available in coffee houses such as the Sultan's Head or Edward Lloyd's. They were male preserves, redolent with the smell of roasting coffee blended with smoke and heated conversation. Thomas Garroway's coffee house in Exchange Alley advertised tea as being:

> *"good against crudities, strengthening the weakness of the Ventricle or Stomach, causing good Appetite and Digestion and particularly for Men of a corpulent Body and such as are great eaters of flesh."*

Some of these tea and coffee houses became places of business as well as pleasure. Institutions such as Christies, Sotheby's and Lloyd's Underwriters developed from these establishments as did our custom of gratuitously rewarding waiters and wenches by putting money into boxes marked T.I.P. in order To Insure Promptness.

There was just one company that was responsible for supplying this growing demand for tea; the Honourable East India Company.

RUTHLESSNESS TO RICHES

The East India Company was granted its original charter by Elizabeth I in 1600. English traders were amongst the first to open up the sea route round the Cape of Good Hope to China and Japan and were avid to raid the rich treasure trove of exotic produce and artifacts which those new lands harboured. The profits looked to be fabulous and James I was quick to grant the charter in perpetuity.

Tea was one of the early cargoes and the commercial success of the East India Company was closely linked to the developing trade in tea. The commercial practices of the EIC make one blush: listen to this.

The Company wanted tea which was becoming very popular in Britain and was therefore a very, very lucrative commodity. The Chinese would only sell tea in exchange for silver: this meant that English coffers were being drained of that precious metal.

The Company decided that its best option was to force the Chinese to buy opium from India (the British were growing a lot of opium in India) for silver. That way, there would be plenty of silver (in India and therefore in British purses) with which to buy the tea from China.

It took three wars, the infamous Opium Wars, and the deaths of many thousands of Chinese to persuade China of the desirability of this way of doing business and, as a result of this disgraceful trade, the British had succeeded in turning a quarter of the Chinese population into addicts.

SWEET SUCCESS

It was not just the importation of tea that was so profitable. The English tooth was sweet and imports of sugar rose with the growth of the tea-drinking habit. When Charles II regained his throne in 1660, England imported less than 100 tons. Forty years later this figure had risen to an enormous 10,000 tons.

During the 18th century, tea began to outweigh coffee in popularity: the reason for this is that tea began to become part of English domestic social life – it began to be drunk at home. Whilst men still enjoyed the club atmosphere of the tea and coffee shops, their ladies, their wives and daughters, would serve it to their friends or to their families and guests after dinner.

Some people had difficulty adapting to its use. Sir Walter Scott tells the story of:

"how the Lady Pumphraston, to whom a pound of fine green tea had been sent as a rare and valuable present, served it us with melted butter, as condiment to a salted rump of beef, and complained that no cooking she could contrive would make these foreign greens tender."

(From Curtis's *Botanical Magazine*)

It is in this period that tea made its first recorded appearance at Heligan. In April 1717 Squire Lewis is recorded as having purchased Bohee tea and a canister from Mr Vallack and, only three days later, a pound of tea from Samuel Marder. Lewis and his wife also had a taste for coffee for in May of the same year they took a trip to Exeter for Mary to consult doctors and surgeons, and they purchased both ground coffee and green tea. They also visited coffee houses, at three pence a time, and perhaps it was the fashionable china in these establishments that prompted Squire Lewis's purchase of 'China-ware' for £3 15s, together with copper saucepans, teapots and canisters.

These visits did little good; Mary died just two years later.

TEA AT HELIGAN

In the archives at Heligan there are three small, leather-bound books. These are Grace Tremayne's diaries for the years 1774 to 1777. Writing in black ink in a fine, neat hand, she records such details as:

"Friday 7th (January 1774) *Captain Creed and Mr Nicolls of the 33rd dined here. Mrs Ball drank tea here, Mr King went away after breakfast."*

And the custom was not limited to Heligan House.

"Friday 11th (February 1774) *Mr Peard drank tea at Mevagissy."*

"Friday 25th (March 1774) *My brother drank tea at Dr Gould's."*

These diaries record no dramatic events, no local disasters or occurrences of national importance, but what Grace does tell us in her quiet, brief way is that, by 1774, tea-drinking was an established habit amongst the gentry of Cornwall. What she also tells us is that it was drunk after the main meal, which was taken in the late afternoon, and on social occasions when visitors called.

TEA TO CAMELLIAS
The tea-drinking habit was firmly established and the trade lucrative. The directors of the East India Company wanted more than just a trading relationship with China. They wanted to set up their own plantations in England's own colonies and thus increase their own control and their own profits. Understandably, the Chinese were anxious to protect their unique position; they jealously guarded their prized plants and were unwilling to part with them.

There is a story that the local people of Canton, which was where the Honourable East India Company was based, attempted to foil the export of tea plants by substituting the decorative *Camellia japonica* for the tea plant, *Camellia sinensis*. If true, it is a pretty example of Chinese naivety to consider that such a simple subterfuge would fool the foreign devils who were prepared to go to such formidable lengths to secure their supplies of tea.

During the search for tea plants, some of the EIC employees, notably John Reeves who was a tea inspector, came across the decorative camellias in the gardens around Canton and it was these garden varieties that were sent back to England.

RICH HUSBANDS
Ship owners, ship husbands as they were called, were rich. They had rich friends. There were enormous profits to be made from the ownership and sponsoring of ships. There were other advantages too. One of these was the opportunity to acquire luxuries and curiosities that were brought home in addition to the main cargoes.

Officers on the East Indiamen were allowed a small amount of storage space for private goods. This was usually situated below the tea chests and therefore could only accommodate non-perishable goods, however some captains who had either a special interest or a commission from a wealthy patron, contrived to bring back some live camellias. It was a difficult business. The East India ships set out from London in January and arrived in China in September when they took on their cargo of tea. Heavily laden, the return journey took a year. The plants were far more likely to be trampled during loading, crushed by shifting cargo, to expire from lack of water or from too much by being washed overboard, rather than arrive safe at their destination, but survive they did, just a few.

CAPTAINS AND CAMELLIAS

The first recorded camellias to be imported by the sea captains of the East India Company were C. j. 'Alba Plena' a pure white, formal double flower and C. j 'Variegata' a semi-double with red and white blotched petals. They were both brought back on the three-masted East Indiaman *Carnatic*, commanded by Captain James Corner.

The arrival of these exotic plants caused great excitement.

C. j. 'Alba Plena' from the Chandler & Booth catalogue 1831

C. j. 'Variegata' from the Chandler & Booth catalogue 1831

Samuel Curtis in his *Monograph on the Genus Camellia* describes the camellia:

"The Japan Rose ... was long held in the highest estimation by the Chinese and Japanese ... and is a tree of considerable size, with ash coloured bark, and most beautiful shining evergreen leaves.

Just as the dawn is the harbinger of the morning and the sun does not at once reach his meridian glory, so the Camellias advance on us in degrees of beauty ... they seem to strike the eye with dazzling perfection, and we cannot but view with admiration the diversity and elegance of this beautiful family of plants, which the all-wise and bountiful hand of God seems to have formed for the delight of mankind".

No wonder everybody wanted one!

Illustration from Samuel Curtis's *Monograph on the Genus Camellia*

More camellias followed. Sir Robert
Preston, who brought back C. *j.* 'Rubra
Plena' in 1794, was principal owner of
nine ships. Sir Abraham Hume, principal
owner of the *Hope* under Captain James
Pendergrass brought back C. *j.* 'Incarnata'
in 1806. Captain Wellbeck of the
Cuffnells brought back C. *j.* 'Paeoniiflora'
in 1811. Captain Richard Rawes who
commanded the *Warren Hastings* was
fortunate. The principal owner, William
Sims, had little interest in camellias, so
that Richard Rawes was able to name his
most famous introduction, *Camellia
reticulata* 'Captain Rawes' after himself,
thus assuring his place in history.

Camellia reticulata 'Captain Rawes' from the
Chandler & Booth catalogue 1831

THE CAMELLIA IN ENGLAND

These were not the first camellias to arrive in England. Known as the Chinese or Japanese
Rose, the first recorded live plants belonged to Lord Petrie of Thornton Hall in Essex and
were painted by George Edwards, included as background in a picture of a pheasant.

A PICTURE PAINTS A THOUSAND WORDS.

Camellias were exotic and thought to be
too tender to survive our climate so that
these first plants were kept in hot houses,
stove houses as they were called. Lord
Petrie's gardener, Mr James Gordon, is
reputed eventually to have killed the
original ones by keeping them too warm
but fortunately not before many cuttings
had been taken. It was, however, the
garden varieties imported from China that
started the passion for camellias.

Stylized camellias in George Edward's painting
of a Chinese Pheasant

Sixteen camellias had been imported into England by 1820. They continued to be treated as tender plants until well after the mid-19th century and, although much coveted by collectors, it was only the wealthy who could afford to keep them; people like the Duke of Devonshire who built in 1811 a large and splendid conservatory at Chiswick House. Originally intended for fruit, from 1828 it housed his collection of camellias, some of which still survive.

If the first camellias brought into this country went to private collectors, subsequent imports found their way to the Horticultural Society of London (later the Royal Horticultural Society) and to the commercial nurseries including Knight & Perry's Royal Exotic Nursery, William Rollisson & Sons, and Chandler & Booth who had their premises on the Vauxhall Road. It was these men who began to study the camellia, to experiment, to hybridize, to grow thousands of seedlings from which to select those whose names became famous over the next twenty years: C. j. 'Anemoniflora', C. j. 'Althaeiflora' and C. j. 'Chandleri' are still grown today.

FLOWERS OF FASHION

Camellias were becoming all the rage. They were highly desirable as conservatory plants and increasingly popular as florists' flowers for button holes and corsages. They featured in artifacts brought back from China, in paintings, printed fabrics and wallpaper, and these designs were copied in England. The iconic palace, the Brighton Pavilion built by Prinny, Queen Victoria's eldest son, in the 1820s, is decorated with wallpapers, painted panels and wall paintings that depict camellias in both natural and stylized forms.

England was changing and changing fast. As the century progressed, increasing wealth and urbanisation was creating a whole new class of people with their own gardens and the money to indulge their interests. There was a market for horticultural novelties that the nurseries were ever willing and anxious to supply.

In 1831 Chandler & Booth listed 35 different cultivars: by 1875 there were thousands. Camellias were the flowers of fashion.

Wall panel from the Brighton Pavilion

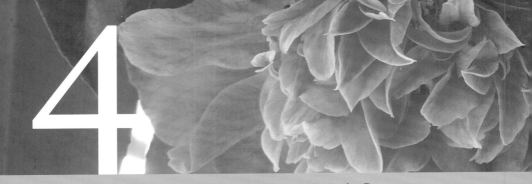

HELIGAN'S CAMELLIAS

There are over seventy camellias in the Heligan Collection, all planted before 1920. They represent over a century of camellia history and divide into three periods. The early period covers the years from the very late 18th century to the mid-19th century and includes some of the original imports from China and the new cultivars raised from them by English nurserymen. The second period covers the second half of the 19th century and mainly represents camellias raised on the Continent. The third period covers the years from the turn of the century to 1920.

IDENTIFICATION

There was an enormous enthusiasm for camellias during the 19th century. Hundreds of new cultivars were produced, many of them almost indistinguishable from each other, and the majority of these dropped out of cultivation after the 1880s.

This causes problems when trying to identify the camellias in an old Collection such as that at Heligan. Camellias can be difficult to identify anyway. The flowers of the same cultivars can vary: plants perform differently in response to their growing conditions and there are rarely garden records to help.

The identification of the unnamed camellias at Heligan has been attempted by comparison with contemporaneous literature and illustrations. Three sources in particular were used: the Chandler & Booth catalogue of 1831, the catalogues of Ambroise Verschaffelt's nursery in Ghent, *Nouvelle Iconographie des Camellias*, thirteen volumes from 1848 to 1860, and the works of Abbé Berlèse, *Iconographie du Genre Camellia* published in 1841. From these sources, a list of possibilities was compiled. Then, by studying the English nursery lists to discover what was available at the time, possibilities became probabilities. These nursery lists include those from Knight & Perry's Royal Exotic Nursery, James Veitch & Sons, William Rollisson & Sons and William Bull. The final step was to search for living examples of these old cultivars, not only in England but in France, Italy, Switzerland and New Zealand. For all that, this method of identification is by no means foolproof.

THE EARLY YEARS

The oldest camellias at Heligan are likely to have been planted by John Hearle Tremayne, whose career as an MP gave him access to the London nurseries. Foremost amongst these was Chandler and Buckingham who published a catalogue of their camellias in 1825. Buckingham was soon to be replaced by William Beattie Booth, a Cornishman who was recognized as a leading expert on camellias. He presented two papers to the Royal Horticultural Society and was unusual in being admitted to fellowship of the Society, normally reserved for the landed gentry: he is listed as Garden Clerk. Before going to London to join the Chandler nursery, William Beattie Booth was head gardener to Sir Charles Lemon at Carclew, the family with which the Tremaynes were later to be closely related through marriage and it is perhaps through this connection that Heligan obtained its first camellias.

In 1831, Alfred Chandler published his second catalogue that listed sixteen original imports from China and nineteen English varieties raised from these introductions. The descriptions are the work of William Beattie Booth.

Heligan has five plants that are featured in these two early catalogues and have been identified by comparison with Alfred Chandler's original illustrations.

THE CONTINENTAL CAMELLIAS

During the second period up to the turn of the century, the impetus for developing new camellias came from the Continent and it is these cultivars that form the main part of the Heligan Collection. The sources for attempting to identify them are also from the Continent. The works of Abbé Berlèse listed 282 different cultivars and are extraordinary in the detail and accuracy of the descriptions and illustrations. The catalogues of the Verschaffelt nursery in Ghent, published annually from 1848 to 1860, described 623 cultivars and although not as detailed are, none the less, invaluable.

A few of these camellias are still well-known today. The identification of the remainder has been the subject of much research. Only two of the Heligan camellias, one in the Northern Gardens and one at Heligan House, had retained their labels. There are no garden records apart from a few pages of a notebook written by Commander Thomas, a tenant of the estate during the middle of the last century. Some of the identifications recorded in this notebook were made by the Australian expert, Professor E G Waterhouse, who visited the gardens in 1950.

The camellias in this second period were planted during the time that John Tremayne was squire at Heligan.

20TH CENTURY CAMELLIAS

There are only four camellias in the gardens dating from the 20th century, planted by John Claude (Jack), all well-known cultivars. By this time camellias had very much fallen out of fashion, superseded by the nationwide passion for rhododendrons, and although this was to change in the 1930s after the introduction of new camellia species and the hybrids that were developed from them, it was too late for Heligan, the last squire, John Claude, having left the estate to live in Italy.

5

CAMELLIA TOUR OF
THE NORTHERN GARDENS

This chapter takes you on a tour of the Northern Gardens, pointing out the old camellias of the Collection that are of special interest and telling what is known of their history. Where appropriate, the original illustration from which identification was made is shown.

As you come into the garden, the first camellia on the Western Ride is C. j. 'Althaeiflora'.

Camellia 25   *Camellia japonica* **'Althaeiflora'**

The flowers of this camellia are a glowing red. It was raised by Alfred Chandler in 1819, a seedling of an early Chinese introduction, C. j. 'Anemoniflora'. William Beattie Booth tells us that it was so named because of its resemblance to a large double red hollyhock. The inner petaloids, which are mutated stamens, clearly show the shape and the tiny white tip of parent C. j. 'Anemoniflora'.

C. j. 'Althaeiflora'

C. j. 'Althaeiflora' from the Chandler & Booth catalogue 1831

CAMELLIA TOUR OF THE NORTHERN GARDENS

1. C25 *C. japonica* 'Althaeiflora'
2. C24 *C. j.* 'Gloire de Nantes'
3. C17 *C. j.* name unknown
4. C85 *C. j.* 'Sacco Vera'
5. C84 *Camellia cuspidata*
6. C14 *C. j.* 'Lavinia Maggi'
7. C80 *C. j.* 'Albertii'
8. C10 *C. j.* 'Madame Martin Cachet'
9. C77 *C. j.* 'Auguste Delfosse'

10. C6 *C. j.* 'Anemoniflora'
11. C5 *C. j.* possibly 'Teutonia'
12. C4 *C. j.* name unknown
13. C2 *C. j.* 'Dianthiflora'
14. C1 *C. j.* possibly 'Aspasia'
15. C72 *C. j.* name unknown
16. C71 *C. j.* 'Amalia Servi'
17. C65 *C. j.* 'Anemoniflora'?
18. C64 *C. j.* 'Leeana Superba'
19. C63 *C. j.* 'Perle des Camellias'
20. Three young plants of
    C. reticulata 'Captain Rawes'
21. C87 *C. reticulata* stump
22. C86 *C. rusticana* 'Beni-arajishi'
23. C49 *C. rusticana*
24. C47 *C. j.* 'Rubens'
25. C46 *C. j.* 'Bella di Firenze'
26. C50 *C. j.* 'Rafia'
27. C54 *C. sasanqua* 'Alba'
28. C55 *C. sasanqua* 'Rosea'
29. C57 *C. j.* 'Gloire de Nantes Variegated'
30. C45 *C. j.* 'Fleur de Peche'
31. C44 *C. j.* 'Eugenie de Massena'
32. C41 *C. j.* 'Mary Thomas (Heligan)'
33. C40 *C. j.* name unknown
34. C36 *C. j.* 'Arciduchessa Augusta'
35. C35 *C. j.* 'Auguste Delfosse'
36. C33 *C. j.* name unknown
37. C29 *C. j.* 'Valtevareda'
38. C26 *C. j.* name unknown
39. C52 *C. j.* 'Alba Plena'

Camellias in the Jungle (shown on Jungle map)
C1 *C. j.* 'Paul's Jupiter'
C2 *C. j.* 'Donckelaeri'
C3 *Camellia japonica* on Butler's Path

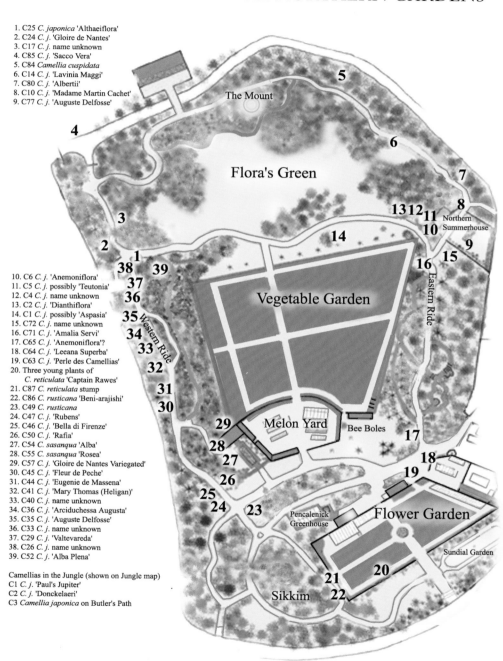

The Mount

Flora's Green

Northern Summerhouse

Vegetable Garden

Eastern Ride

Western Ride

Melon Yard

Bee Boles

Pencalenick Greenhouse

Flower Garden

Sundial Garden

Sikkim

✿ *Turning to the left up Western Ride the next camellia is C. j. 'Gloire de Nantes'.*

Camellia 24

This camellia is one of the pleasures of the winter garden and is affectionately known as the Christmas camellia, so early does it bloom. The first blossoms often appear in December and by the New Year the tree is lit up by brave, bright blooms, shining against the dark luxuriant foliage.

The flowers are semi-double, the petals twisted around spoon-shaped petaloids interspersed with scattered stamens. C. j. 'Gloire de Nantes' was raised in 1894 by the Guichard Soeurs nursery in Nantes, a leading French nursery of the time.

Camellia japonica 'Gloire de Nantes'

C. j. 'Gloire de Nantes'

✿ *On the other side of the path and stretching across to Flora's Green is Camellia 17, one of the most beautiful camellias in the gardens. Every spring its branches are bent almost to breaking point by the weight of its blooms. The flowers are formal doubles, pale shell-pink; the petals are veined with deeper pink and edged with white.*

Camellia 17   *Camellia japonica* unknown

This camellia has been the subject of much research but its identification remains elusive. Pictorially, the best match is C. j. 'Teutonia var Amabilis' raised in Belgium in 1855 but listings in the English catalogues are inconclusive.

Camellia 17

C. j. 'Teutonia var Amabilis' from the Verschaffelt catalogue of 1855.

At the top of Western Ride is Camellia 85, thought to be C. j. 'Sacco Vera'.

Camellia 85   *Camellia japonica* (thought to be) 'Sacco Vera'

This camellia is now outside the garden proper on the Service Road but just visible over the green gates. It is a densely foliated plant with the lower branches reaching to the ground. The formal double flowers are a delicate pink, the outer petals recurving as the flower ages whilst the inner petals are paler, almost white with a lustrous, pearly sheen.

The Australian expert, Professor Waterhouse, identified a plant of *C. j.* 'Sacco Vera' at Heligan and the flower closely resembles the Abbé Berlèse illustration of 1843, although is slightly different from other depictions.

C. j. 'Sacco Vera'

C. j. 'Sacco Vera', *Berlèse Iconographie du Genre Camellia* 1843

 Turn east at the top of Western Ride, past Dovecote Lawn with its huge Magnolia campbellii, and you are on Beacon Path. There are just four old camellias along this path; several have been lost from the original planting. On the left is Camellia 84, a species camellia, Camellia cuspidata.

Camellia 84   *Camellia cuspidata*

Its delicate, single, white flowers are faintly scented. This camellia was first discovered in China by Augustine Henry: later E H Wilson sent it to Veitch's Coombe Wood Nursery in 1901. Jack Tremayne probably purchased it from there, together with other Wilson introductions including *Davidia involucrata* and *Rhododendron ririei*, both of which can still be seen in the gardens.

Young plant of *Camellia cuspidata*

The only historical record of this camellia at Heligan comes from a report of the 1950 RHS Camellia and Magnolia Tour that contains the following sentence:

> *"We also noted a bush of the small white Camellia cuspidata flowering very freely."*

✿ *Just past the Mount on the right-hand side are two continental camellias. Camellia 15 is pale pink with a white stripe and is yet unidentified. Next to it, by the grassy entrance onto Flora's Green, is Camellia 14, one of the best-known and loved varieties from the mid 19th century.*

Camellia 14

It is a huge old camellia, stretching several yards onto the grass from the path and up into the canopy of rhododendrons above, and it shows remarkable vigour for its age. Most of the flowers are formal doubles with a few rose doubles showing scattered stamens. The colour is pure white with dashes of deep pink and carmine. In most seasons it shows a characteristic red sport.

C. j. 'Lavinia Maggi' was raised in Italy and described by van Houtte in 1858. Originally it was called C. j. 'Contessa Lavinia Maggi' but has since lost its aristocratic appellation.

Camellia japonica 'Lavinia Maggi'

C. j. 'Lavinia Maggi' with red sport C. j. 'Lavinia Maggi Rosea'

✿ *Towards the end of Beacon Path, just before the Northern Summerhouse garden are two old camellias. On the right, Camellia 12 has very small, deep red striped flowers, not yet identified and to the left, one of the largest camellias in the gardens, thought to be C. j. 'Albertii'.*

Camellia 80   *Camellia japonica* (thought to be) 'Albertii'

The flower is a peony, very pale, almost white when it first comes out, but deepens in colour to a pale pink as the flower ages. The petals are streaked with deeper pink and carmine. Alfred Chandler obtained this cultivar from China. It first bloomed in 1839 and was named in honour of Albert, Prince Consort.

This tree regularly bears sports that reverse the main colours, that is, deep pink with white streaks.

C. j. 'Albertii'

Pink sport of C. j. 'Albertii'

At the end of Beacon Path you enter the Northern Summerhouse garden, with its pretty brick summerhouse and its wide view over the grisilinia hedge towards the sea. On the right of the summerhouse, pruned to form a backdrop to the little flower border, is C. j. 'Madame Martin Cachet'.

Camellia 10   *Camellia japonica* 'Madame Martin Cachet'

The flower is a showy peony, deep pink, with more than two hundred petals and petaloids.

C. j. 'Madame Martin Cachet' was introduced by Bahuaud-Litou 1914-20. If this was planted by Jack Tremayne it must have been one of the last he planted before leaving for Italy in about 1923.

C. j. 'Madame Martin Cachet'

✿ *South of the formal pool is Camellia 77, a small compact fastigate tree that shows signs of considerable damage. This is C. j. 'Auguste Delfosse'*

Camellia 77

Camellia japonica 'Auguste Delfosse'

C. j. 'Auguste Delfosse'

The flower is a formal double, with well-imbricated petals giving the appearance of a star-shape. Deep red in colour, each petal has several white bands down each side of the midrib.

It was first described by Verschaffelt who obtained the seed from Belgium and it was named for the President of the Belgium Chamber of Representatives, Monsieur A Delfosse.

This cultivar proved very popular and appeared in all the catalogues studied. Prices differed greatly. In 1873 the Veitch nursery offered *"Nice young healthy plants"* at 90s per dozen: William Rollisson & Sons offered single plants for 7s 6d, while William Bull clearly went for the top end of the market, selling plants 1ft 9inches high for 21s and a 3ft plant for 42s, more than a month's pay for the gardener who would have planted it out!

✿ *On leaving the Northern Summerhouse garden, you must make a detour from the guidebook route to see the camellias planted along the south side of Flora's Green. The first is one of the oldest camellias at Heligan, probably planted by John Hearle Tremayne before 1850.*

Camellia 6

Camellia japonica 'Anemoniflora'

In the Chandler & Booth catalogue of 1831, William Beattie Booth tells us that this cultivar was imported for the Royal Garden at Kew in 1806, directly from China. The tree is remarkably vigorous, spreading almost to the back of the little summerhouse. Every year it bears great numbers of flowers that show a variety of forms from single flowers with a boss of stamens to a form that is much nearer to the Chandler & Booth illustration.

C. j. 'Anemoniflora'

This camellia was greatly prized for its ability to set seed and it was by careful cross-pollination with other camellias that nurserymen raised many valuable new cultivars.

C. j. 'Anemoniflora' from the Chandler & Booth catalogue 1831

 Next is Camellia 5, one of the continental cultivars.

Camellia 5

The flowers are a very full formal double, candy-pink with a white stripe down the centre of each petal. The plant also bears a white sport. The identification of this is uncertain, the nearest is *C. j.* 'Teutonia', raised in Germany in 1841, known and available in England as *C. j.* 'Victoria and Albert' but there is no corroboration for this suggestion and its mystery remains unsolved.

Camellia japonica unknown

Camellia 5

C. j. 'Teutonia' from Abbé *Berlèse Iconographie du Genre Camellia*

White sport of Camellia 5

🌸 *Next to Camellia 5 is a single red japonica.*

Camellia 4 *Camellia japonica*

This is a magnificent specimen with shapely single flowers and elegant foliage. Impressive as it is, it is likely to be the original rootstock on which a more decorative scion was once grafted. The scion has since died, leaving the understock to flourish.

Single Red *Camellia japonica*

🌸 *Planted close to the Single Red along the Flora's Green path is another of the very early camellias, just a scrap left, barely alive. This is C. j. 'Dianthiflora', also known as C. j. 'Insignis'*

Camellia 2 *Camellia japonica* 'Dianthiflora' syn 'Insignis'

The flower is a semi-double, deep glowing red, with a prominent crown of stamens, many of which have been converted into petaloids, striped and spotted with red.

C. j. 'Dianthiflora' was raised in 1822 by Knight & Perry's Royal Exotic Nursery in the Kings Road, Chelsea, from seeds of C. j. 'Anemoniflora'. There is a link to Heligan here: John Tremayne was a customer of the Knight nursery and the Tremaynes continued to buy from the nursery after it was taken over by Veitch in about 1850.

C. j. 'Dianthiflora' does not feature in any of the English catalogues, but in the Chandler & Booth catalogue there is an illustration of a camellia called C. j. 'Insignis'.

C. j. 'Insignis' from the Chandler & Booth catalogue 1831

C. j. 'Dianthiflora' syn 'Insignis'

The flower shows a close similarity to the Heligan one and William Beattie Booth notes in his text that this camellia is likely to be the same as *C. j.* 'Knight's Carnation Waratah', which itself appears in Loddiges *Botanical Cabinet* as *C. j.* 'Knightii' and in Loudon's *Hortus Britannicus* as No. 19 *C. j.*' Dianthiflora', thus illustrating the degree of confusion that exists in the early records.

Under which name it was originally purchased it is impossible to know but this is likely to be one of the oldest camellias in the garden.

There is very little new growth on this camellia and just two cuttings have been rooted. Through these this old and rare cultivar will survive.

Cutting of *C. j.* 'Dianthiflora' showing less than 2 cms of new growth

Just outside the Vegetable Garden is Camellia 1, a dark pink formal double, with a white stripe down each petal, as yet unidentified, although it bears a close resemblance to a well-authenticated plant, C. j. 'Aspasia' at Tregrahen Gardens.

Returning to the guidebook route, down Eastern Ride there are eight old camellias, only three of which are of any significance. The rest, single to semi-double reds and pinks, and pretty enough in themselves, are not sufficiently distinctive to identify and may well be the rootstocks from which the original grafted scions have disappeared.

Camellia 72

The first of what are obviously garden cultivars is a strong pink peony at the top of Eastern Ride. Although so far it has defied all attempts at identification, it is a magnificent plant, with luxuriant foliage and it is unusual in that it produces cutting material throughout the year.

Camellia japonica unknown

Camellia 72

Almost opposite is an Italian cultivar.

Camellia 71   *Camellia japonica* (thought to be) 'Amalia Servi'

Quite small for its age, Camellia 71 is a delicate tree with a pendulous habit and open arching growth that trails to the ground. It is planted well back from the Eastern Ride and marks the position of a former path, probably that proposed by Thomas Grey at the end of the 18th century. The flowers are a large, shapely formal double, deep pink with a pronounced white stripe down the centre of most of the petals and the leaves noticeably bullate. There is a similar camellia in the Sundial Garden at the back of the border where its branches overhang the lane to the Steward's House.

C. j. 'Amalia Servi'

The only suggested name for these camellias came from a distinguished Italian camellia expert. C. j. 'Amalia Servi' is illustrated in the Verschaffelt catalogue of 1856 and shows the rounded, bullate leaves that are a feature of the Heligan plant. The name, however, does not appear in any of the English nursery lists studied and, until a living example can be found for comparison, identification remains speculative.

C. j. 'Amalia Servi' from the Verschaffelt catalogue of 1856

 At the bottom of Eastern Ride are Camellias 65 and 64.

Camellia 65   *Camellia japonica* 'Anemoniflora'?

This is one of the oldest and largest camellias in the garden and it is a puzzle. It has been identified as C. j. 'Anemoniflora' and clearly it is an anemoniform, many of the flowers showing the converted petaloids that are a key feature of C. j. 'Anemoniflora' but the colour, number of petals and even the leaves do not accord with the Chandler & Booth description.

There are no early illustrations that match this flower, perhaps it is a seedling that did not attain lasting popularity, so the descriptive name of *Camellia japonica anemoniflora pink* will have to suffice.

C. j. 'Anemoniflora'?

Camellia 64

Camellia japonica 'Leeana Superba'

C. j. 'Leeana Superba'

This is a fascinating camellia. It is in an odd position, planted amongst the roots of the huge oak at the bottom of Eastern Ride. It is small but its growth must have been much restricted by the tree, depriving it of both water and nutrients, so its age is difficult to determine. It cannot be one of the originals – it is too small and in the wrong place. Who would have planted it there?

There is a similar plant outside the walled garden at Tremough, site of Richard Gill's nursery near Falmouth. This one is huge with a trunk as thick as an elephant's leg; an old, old tree and therefore an old cultivar.

In trying to identify this camellia, therefore, it was necessary to go back to the oldest cultivars and in Abbé Berlèse's *Iconographie du Genre Camellia* there is this illustration for C. j. 'Leeana Superba'.

Abbé Berlèses's 'Leeana Superba'

This cultivar was not raised in England but imported from Japan, originally to Belgium in 1829 where it was named for the London horticulturalist Mr Lee, and then by John Reeves, through Macao, in 1831 where it was named C. j. 'Bealii' It was by this name that the camellia was offered in the English catalogues of Veitch and Rollisson but William Bull offered both!

C. j. 'Leeana Superba' bloomed in the glasshouses of the Verschaffelt nursery in Ghent on April 17 1834.

So how did this very beautiful, brilliant red camellia come to Heligan?

The position of the Heligan plant perhaps gives a clue. It is close to what used to be a nursery area: you can still see several plants of *R. griersonianum* and five *Trachycarpus fortunei* that were lined out here towards the end of the First World War, waiting to be planted out, but the gardeners never

C. j. 'Leeana Superba' beneath the oak

came back. Was this camellia one of those plants waiting to be put out into the garden?

There is some evidence that Jack Tremayne bought plants from Richard Gill. Was this one of them, propagated from the one on the wall at Tremough and left close to the old oak? The oak tree is hollow and may well have to come down before too long. When it does, will there be the remnants of a clay pot amongst the roots?

❀ *Close to C. j.* 'Leeana Superba', *arching over the little brick building known as the Bothy is a curious camellia, the most unusual one in the garden.*

Camellia 63   *Camellia japonica* (possibly) 'Perle des Camellias'

This pretty, spreading tree is planted in a small bed at the bottom of Eastern Ride. The flower is unusual, halfway between peony and anemone form with a few scattered stamens. Most of these stamens are fused together with the stile and the central petaloids are twisted round this central column. The flowers from new cuttings have many more petals than the old ones. The leaves are both curled and variegated, having a paler area along the centre vein. The curling leaf is very distinctive and appears to be of viral origin.

C. j. 'Perle des Camellias'

This is a most unusual plant: none of the camellia experts who have visited Heligan has been able to suggest a name. The only tentative suggestion comes from Italy, *C. j.* 'Perle des Camellias', described in Abbé Berlèse's *Monographie du Genre Camellia*, 1838. The name does not appear in the nursery lists studied and there is no other corroboration.

The description of *C. j.* 'Perle des Camellias' in the International Camellia Register is rather vague but does not preclude this from being the correct identification. There is, however, no mention of the curled leaves and this rarity remains a mystery.

❀ *As you continue west, you arrive at the entrance to the Flower Garden, flanked by the Banana House on one side and a huge R. falconeri on the other. The high brick wall, through which the door is cut, once supported the most famous of all Heligan's camellias, Camellia reticulata* 'Captain Rawes'.

Captain Richard Rawes of the Honourable East India Company brought home a plant for his friend Thomas Carey Palmer in 1820. Four years later, more plants were brought in for the Royal Horticultural Society by their collector John Dampier Parks: the first of these flowered in 1829. John Hearle Tremayne brought two plants down to Cornwall: one was planted against the outside wall of the Flower Garden, next to the Head Gardener's office. It was this camellia that grew to mighty proportions: in 1896, it was described as:

"*a very old plant* (that) *bears hundreds of huge flowers annually:*"

(Gardeners Chronicle 1896, article by J Walker)

Half a century later the wall had to be raised to support its immense height and spread but sadly storms brought down this magnificent camellia before restoration work had started.

There was another *C. reticulata* 'Captain Rawes' planted against the west-facing outside wall of the Flower Garden in the area now known as Sikkim. This plant survived until just a few years ago but was finally choked to death by the surrounding rampant rhododendrons. Although dead, the tree has left a little mystery. The cultivar is difficult to propagate by cuttings and has to be

Young plant of *C. reticulata* 'Captain Rawes'

grafted. The original rootstock is beginning to grow: it will be interesting to allow this to flower to see exactly which rootstock was used.

There are several young plants of *C. reticulata* 'Captain Rawes' espalied against the inside wall of the Flower Garden.

✿ *Next to the old C. reticulata 'Captain Rawes' is another camellia planted close to the wall. This is a Chinese cultivar, Camellia rusticana 'Beni-arajishi' from 1859. The name translates as 'Fierce Lion' and it is a well-known and distinctive variety.*

Camellia 86   *Camellia rusticana* 'Beni-arajishi'

Its trunk is curiously twisted; it looks as though it was originally espalied (you can see old nails in the brickwork) but the branches have long since broken away from their wires. The trunk now has a plaited appearance as if several branches have been twisted

and fused together. Growth is severely restricted on the western side by rhododendrons planted in this area and the beautiful deep red, peony-shaped flowers can only be seen from the Flower Garden. The leaves are distinctive, long and narrow with a slender cuspidate tip; the numerous frilled petals and petaloids twist round a few scattered stamens. This camellia produces a sport, red variegated with white, known as *Camellia rusticana* 'Arajishi'.

Camellia rusticana 'Beni-arajishi'

❀ *As you leave Sikkim to go north up the Western Ride Camellia 49 is on the corner of the path leading towards the Italian Garden.*

Camellia 49   *Camellia rusticana*

This camellia is remarkable not for its flower, a single pink, but for its form: it has an unusual prostrate habit, with lax, pliant growth. There is a subspecies of japonica, *C. rusticana*, known as the snow camellia and this is thought to be a type of *C. rusticana*.

Camellia rusticana

❀ *Close to Camellia 49 is the splendid Camellia 47.*

Camellia 47   *Camellia japonica* 'Rubens'

Its many flowers are full formal doubles, deep pink with a broad white stripe down the centre to the tip of the petals.

There is some confusion here. This camellia has been identified as C. *j.* 'Duc de Bretagne' by comparison with a well-authenticated plant in one of the National Collections, but there was always a concern with this because it is very different from the illustration of 'Duc de Bretagne' in the Verschaffelt catalogue for 1848. A recent study of the same cultivar in Brittany shows a flower that closely resembles the Verschaffelt illustration. So, adhering to the methodology of comparison with original illustrations and venturing where angels fear to tread, this is C. *j.* 'Rubens', raised by van Houtte in 1854.

C. *j.* 'Rubens'   C. *j.* 'Rubens' from Verschaffelt 1856

✿ *Next to C. j. 'Rubens' is another continental camellia, C. j. 'Bella di Firenze', flourishing despite being smashed in two many years ago by a falling rhododendron.*

Camellia 46

Camellia japonica 'Bella di Firenze'

C. j. 'Bella di Firenze'

C. j. 'Bella di Firenze' from the Verschaffelt catalogue of 1856

These pink striped camellias are quite common, with very little to distinguish one from another, so a positive identification is difficult. *C. j.* 'Bella di Firenze' was a popular camellia that featured in many of the English catalogues and the Heligan plant is certainly a good match for a well-authenticated version found in France.

✿ *Close to C. j. 'Bella di Firenze' is Camellia 50, planted at the back of the Western Ride border so that it also forms part of the border in the Italian Garden.*

Camellia 50

Camellia japonica (thought to be) 'Rafia'

This camellia is a formal double with rounded, heart-shaped petals and thought to be *C. j.* 'Rafia'. The scant archival evidence for this comes from notes made by Commander Thomas following the visit by Australian expert Professor Waterhouse in 1950. The notes refer to a plant of *C. j.* 'Rafia' near to the Italian Garden. There is no other camellia in that area that matches the description of *C. j.* 'Rafia' and certainly Professor Waterhouse would have known this cultivar in Australia.

C. j. 'Rafia' is featured in the Verschaffelt catalogue for 1857 and was listed in the William Bull list for 1867 and the Veitch list for 1873.

C. j. 'Rafia'   C. j. 'Rafia' from the Verschaffelt
                                                catalogue of 1856

❀ *Two camellias in the Italian Garden, Camellias 54 and 55, are the delight of the*
autumn garden at Heligan.

Camellia 54   *Camellia sasanqua* (probably) 'Alba'

This camellia is more than 12 metres high, but slender and delicate with small slim leaves
and single white flowers, the petals fluted, and with a starburst of yellow stamens. This is
a sasanqua, probably *Camellia sasanqua* 'Alba'. The tree blooms in October and the
flowers have a sweet honey scent that attracts the late bees. *Camellia sasanqua* 'Alba'
was available from William Bull in 1869.

Camellia sasanqua
'Alba' a treat for the
autumn bees

❀ *Next is Camellia 55, another sasanqua, also planted against the walls of the little*
brick summerhouse.

Camellia 55

It has small, single, deep pink flowers amongst the bronze-red young foliage and is thought to be *Camellia sasanqua* 'Rosea'. This was offered by William Rollisson & Sons for 3s 6d in the 1875 catalogue only. It was available from William Bull in 1869 and 1876. If this identification is correct, the apparent limited availability is significant in establishing the age of the plant. Like the previous plant, this camellia flowers in October.

Camellia sasanqua 'Rosea'

C. sasanqua 'Rosea'

Camellia 57, also in the Italian garden is a version of *C. j.* 'Gloire de Nantes'. This tall, rather straggly camellia grows against the back of the summerhouse. The tree is top-heavy and the bottom of the trunk has suffered some damage but there are new shoots coming from the base. The flower is very similar to *C. j.* 'Gloire de Nantes' except that many blooms are marbled white, with white spots or sometimes larger white flakes. This colouration varies from year to year and is viral in nature.

This is the variegated version of *C. j.* 'Gloire de Nantes' or at least a version of 'Gloire de Nantes' that is showing the variegated sport. The sport was not described until 1941 but no doubt plants showed this variegation before that date.

❀ *Continuing up the Western Ride you come to Camellia 45, C. j. 'Fleur de Pêche', the peach blossom camellia.*

Camellia 45
Camellia japonica 'Fleur de Pêche' or 'Fleur Dipater'

This is a low, spreading shrub with dense foliage reaching to ground. It is not as old or as large as some in the Collection but it is, perhaps, smaller than it might otherwise have been since its growth was restricted by a very large rhododendron under which it was planted. The rhododendron has since died and now the camellia is showing signs of more vigorous growth.

The flower is delicate, a small pale pink semi-double with the inner petals twisted around the few stamens: the leaves are large and elegantly shaped. *C. j.* 'Fleur de Pêche' first featured in the Bahuaud-Litou Catalogue of 1914-20.

C. j. 'Fleur de Pêche'

❀ *Close by is Camellia 44, C. j. 'Eugenie de Massena'. This is the only camellia in the garden that retained a label, misspelt as 'Eugenia de Massena' but nonetheless worth its weight in gold!*

Camellia 44

This cultivar was first described in England by William Rollisson & Sons in 1877 and named for the wife of Andre Massena, Duke of Rivoli who was one of Napoleon's marshals. It was a popular variety, appearing in the all the main catalogues.

Camellia japonica 'Eugenie de Massena'

C. j. 'Eugenie de Massena'

❀ *Next to C. j. 'Eugenie de Massena' is Camellia 41, a large camellia with mid-pink formal double flowers, some of which show a definite spiral-shape in the arrangement of the petals. The inner petals are quite pointed and stand erect giving the flower a distinctive appearance.*

HELIGAN'S VERY OWN CAMELLIA!

Camellia 41

This camellia is unique to Heligan, named by Professor E G Waterhouse for Mary, wife of Commander Thomas.

The only clue to the location of this camellia comes from the notes that Commander Thomas left, describing C. j. 'Mary Thomas' as:

'A star-shaped pink just past Eugenia de Massena'.

Camellia japonica 'Mary Thomas (Heligan)'

C. j. 'Mary Thomas (Heligan)'

Some years ago, botanical artist Susan Hillier painted two watercolours of this camellia: the first was a present for Mary Thomas herself, commissioned by her daughters. The second is reproduced here. There is a close likeness between the flower of Camellia 41 (especially those from new cuttings) and Susan Hillier's picture, in particular the shape, the colour, the small white stripes, erect inner petals and acuminate leaves.

C. j. 'Mary Thomas (Heligan)' from a watercolour by Susan Hillier © B Robson

This camellia is likely to be a version of the French cultivar *C. j.* 'L'Avvenire' and is listed in the International Camellia Register as *C. j.* 'Mary Thomas (Heligan)' to differentiate it from a later American camellia by the same name.

❀ *The next camellia of note is Camellia 40. This is one of the largest in the gardens and is one of the few on the Western Ride that has not suffered any significant damage.*

Camellia 40

Camellia japonica **unknown**

The flower is a pink formal double with a white stripe down the centre of each petal and has a distinctive raised center. These camellias are difficult to name: the brief descriptions in the nursery catalogues of the period are insufficient to make any confident identification.

Camellia 40

❀ *The next camellia, Camellia 36, is difficult to see from the path. Once very much bigger, what remains of this camellia is growing from an old stump. Like many of the camellias down the Western Ride, it has suffered considerable damage and is also growing in a poor situation, closely surrounded by other vegetation.*

Camellia 36

Camellia japonica 'Arciduchessa Augusta'

This camellia rarely flowers and when it does, produces only a very few, unformed blooms, rather ragged looking, that do not open fully. All of the petals have a white band down the centre, often split into two or three stripes. The flower fades to a pale mauve.

This camellia was identified by comparison with a similar plant of good provenance at Trewidden. C. j. 'Arciduchessa Augusta' was first described by van Houtte in 1846 and is illustrated in the Verschaffelt catalogue of 1852. The mauve colour of the fading flower is said to resemble the colour that the unfortunate archduchess turned before she died.

C. j 'Arciduchessa Augusta'

The notes that accompany the illustration describe the leaves:

> '....*a foliage which is immediately recognizable by its peculiar form which is oblong-elliptic and tapered-acuminated at both ends.*'

Verschaffelt does not normally mention leaves unless they are a significant characteristic of the plant and the description helps to identify the Heligan plant.

This camellia proved popular in England and appeared in a number of catalogues.

Leaf of Camellia 36

🌼 *Beyond C. j. 'Arciduchessa Augusta' is Camellia 35, another continental cultivar.*

Camellia 35

Tall and spindly, its growth restricted on three sides, its topmost branches are lost in the canopy of surrounding trees. It is the same cultivar as Camellia 77 in the Northern Summerhouse garden, although its shape is very different, probably the combined result of its growing conditions and the damage suffered by Camellia 77.

🌼 *Further on up Western Ride is Camellia 33.*

Camellia japonica 'Auguste Delfosse'

C. j. 'Auguste Delfosse'

Camellia 33

Over ten metres high it is one of the tallest camellias in the gardens. The flower is a single pink with nothing to distinguish it apart from a very prominent golden yellow crown of stamens. This is a rootstock of a grafted hybrid, long since disappeared. It is, however, a handsome flower and an impressive tree that would grace any woodland.

Camellia japonica

Camellia 33

✿ *Moving up Western Ride towards the garden entrance there is a pretty pink striped camellia, Camellia 31, not identified, and next to that, Camellia 29.*

Camellia 29   *Camellia japonica* (thought to be) 'Valtevareda'

This plant has suffered much damage. The surrounding area has been cleared recently and there are signs that this camellia is beginning to regenerate and in a good season it is heavy with blooms.

The flower is a formal double, rich pink with occasional white streaks and is a good pictorial match with *C. j.* 'Valtevareda', featured in the Verschaffelt catalogue of 1853 and with modern cultivars.

C. j. 'Valtevareda' was first raised by Rovelli in 1852 and was available from the William Bull nursery.

C. j. 'Valtevareda'

C. j. 'Valtevareda', Verschaffelt 1853

✿ *The last of the old camellias on Western Ride, close to the garden entrance, is Camellia 26, the identity of which is unknown.*

Camellia 26   *Camellia japonica* unknown

This is a wonderful camellia. Several years ago, it was in very poor condition, its leaves sparse, small and rather yellow. During the last couple of years some of the surrounding vegetation has been cleared and the area mulched. This had brought about a great improvement and the tree is beginning to look much healthier.

What is special about this camellia is the variety of different forms and colours on the same plant: pure white, deep pink with a white edging, white with a faint blush at the base of each petal and parti-coloured flowers, half pink, half white. This poses a problem when trying to identify it: which flower is the original cultivar? There are three peony-forms, deep pink, pale pink, and solid white, reminiscent of the flowers and sports of *C. j.* 'Duchesse Decazes', but the leaves are different.

Many old camellias are chimeras: they contain different strands of genetic material and it is the way in which this genetic material is arranged within the plant that creates a particular form or colouration. If the genetic material becomes disturbed then sports are produced. The original parents are likely to have been a solid pink and a solid white flower; both of these forms occur frequently on this plant. The other flowers that occur are combinations of these two. The most stable form containing both these elements is pale pink with a whitish edging to the petals but it is not sufficiently distinctive to make a confident identification.

Camellia 26

Camellia 26

Camellia 26

❄ *The final camellia in the Northern Gardens is at the top of the Ravine. This very old camellia is perched uncomfortably on top of the stony embankment that forms the west side of the Ravine. Old maps show a path down the side of the Vegetable Garden and it is likely that this camellia was originally planted by the side of that path. Fifty years or more later, about 1910, when this path was dug out and shaped to look like a mountain ravine, the plant was left hanging over the path. The tree is now rather straggly but with some new growth coming from the base. This is C. j. 'Alba Plena'.*

Camellia 52   *Camellia japonica* 'Alba Plena'

C. j. 'Alba Plena' was the first camellia to be brought to England on board an East Indiaman vessel: this was in 1792. It is one of the most beautiful of the white camellias and has retained its popularity for more than 200 hundred years.

In some of the flowers, the edges of the petals show a marked fringing or fimbriation, a mutation from which the variety C. j. 'Fimbriata' is derived, however the fimbriation on the Heligan plant is not as consistent or as fine as one would expect from C. j. 'Fimbriata' so it is probably an 'Alba Plena', with tendencies!

C. j. 'Alba Plena'

CAMELLIAS IN THE JUNGLE

There are only a few old camellias in the Jungle, the scale and topography of the landscape lends itself to more flamboyant planting, but there are three that are worth a mention.

❧ *The first is sited beneath the easterly side of the bridge across Bamboo Pond. This is C. j. 'Paul's Jupiter' raised in 1904.*

Camellia japonica 'Paul's Jupiter'

The camellia has fine deep red single flowers that often set seed.

C. j. 'Paul's Jupiter'

❀ *The second camellia is on the East Flank just below Bamboo Pond and is the Japanese cultivar C. j. 'Masayoshi', known in Europe as C. j. 'Donckelaeri', its name misspelt in every possible way.*

Camellia japonica 'Masayoshi' syn 'Donckelaeri'

It was introduced into Holland from Japan in 1830 by Dr Franz von Siebold.

C. j. 'Masayoshi' syn 'Donckelaeri'

Mr D Beaton, writing in the magazine *The Cottage Gardener* in 1849, tells its story:

"Dr Siebold bought the first of the 'Donklaeri' from Japan along with beautiful lilies and many other fine things that were lost after being landed safely at Antwerp. It so happened that Dr Siebold's cases arrived when the French were besieging the citadel at Antwerp, I believe in 1831; and the place where the cases were put was soon filled with cavalry horses, which knocked everything about in such a way that it was a wonder that a single leaf was saved; and our original camellia 'Donklaeri' was in this melee."

Andre Donckelaer, Chief Gardener at the Botanical Garden of Louvain in Belgium, rescued the plant and, to the ongoing irritation of Japanese camellia enthusiasts, named it for himself. It is one of the finest camellias.

The third and the final camellia of the tour is rather inaccessible, down the steep slope from Butler's Path towards Bamboo Pond. The flowers are single, sugar pink with several inner petals and fused style and stamens.

Single pink camellia, Butler's Path

This is likely to be a root stock but if so, it is an unusual one. Very delicate, very pretty, it has not been identified.

Single pink camellia on Butler's Path

THE RHODODENDRON STORY

RHODODENDRONS IN HISTORY

Rhododendrons came late to England. They are native to many areas of the northern hemisphere and the genus was well-known in the ancient world. The first historical records come from the writings of Xenophon. He was a Greek commander, a former pupil of Socrates who, in 401 BC, was leading 10,000 Greek soldiers back through Kurdistan and Armenia after an unsuccessful campaign in Persia. They came to Cholchis, near to Trazibond in the Black Sea region of northern Turkey. To the soldiers, weary and hungry, humiliated after their defeat, it looked like heaven.

ACCORDING TO XENOPHON:

> *"Fish was available from the nearby seas, the hills were covered with beautiful rhododendrons and the woods harboured rich beehives."*

It was these rich beehives that were to cause the problems. The soldiers saw the hives, stole the honey and guzzled it.

Xenophon describes the scene:

> *"All the soldiers who ate of the honeycomb lost their senses, and were seized with vomiting and purging, none of them being able to stand on their legs. Those who ate but a little were like men very drunk, and those who ate much, like madmen and some like dying persons."*

The honey they had eaten was contaminated with a grayanotoxin from the nectar of the Pontiac Azalea, *Rhododendron luteum*, which was, and still is, widespread in the area.

The plant has a sweet and heavy scent, and although it is the same type of plant that is said to have caused such havoc amongst sweet-toothed soldiers, the problem of toxic honey does not occur in this country, if for no other reasons than that our bees are not adapted to tolerate the toxin and would die before they could accumulate any significant amount of toxin in the hive.

R. luteum, the Pontiac Azalea

RHODODENDRONS COME TO ENGLAND

Rhododendrons first made an impact in England with the introduction in 1763 of *Rhododendron ponticum*. This species is native to the region around the Black Sea, the Balkans and the Iberian Peninsula. Popular initially as a pot-plant, it soon became established as a garden plant, its hardiness and vigour making it highly desirable for woodland planting and to provide cover for game. It also played an important role in early hybridizing experiments.

The delicate flowers of *Rhododendron ponticum.*

The late 18th century saw an unprecedented increase in overseas exploration and commercial activity, due in no small part to the work of one man, clockmaker James Harrison. The determination of longitude at sea was one of the greatest engineering issues of the day and a huge reward was offered to whoever could solve the problem. In 1761, after twenty years of effort during which he designed and engineered several prototypes, Harrison produced a timepiece in which springs and flywheels replaced the pendulum of a conventional clock. This construction enabled the clock to remain accurate to the required 3 seconds per day despite the motion of the ship. His invention changed the history of global trade and exploration, opening up the world to become a market place in which to exchange raw materials and manufactured goods, wealth and ideas.

In 1833 came an invention that made the transport of live plants a possibility. London physician and passionate botanist, Dr Nathanial Ward, invented the Wardian case, an airtight glass case in which live plants could be transported over great distances. The Wardian case revolutionized plant collecting and this, coupled with the development of ships driven by steam, meant that goods could be transported all over the world, regardless of whether the winds were fair or foul.

RHODODENDRON ARBOREUM

Increased commercial activity in India, China, Japan and the Americas resulted in many botanical novelties reaching England and amongst these early 19th century introductions was *R. arboreum*.

The scarlet *R. arboreum* was discovered by Captain Thomas Hardwicke in 1796 while he was on tour of duty in the Himalayas. It bloomed for the first time in 1825 in the garden of The Grange at Alresford in Sussex, an event that caused much excitement in the horticultural world, but it is not Captain Hardwick's name that is remembered. The success of *R. arboreum* is linked to a young man, Joseph Hooker, whose plant-hunting expeditions read like a *Boy's Own* adventure.

The glowing flowers of the red *R. arboreum*

JOSEPH DALTON HOOKER

Joseph Dalton Hooker was born on June 30, 1817 at Halesworth in Suffolk. His father William was a noted botanist, his mother Maria a keen naturalist. More distantly, his relatives included Zacharie Hooker, Vicar of Caerhays in Cornwall and neighbour of the Tremaynes of Heligan. It was from Zacharie's son, Vincent, that Joseph Hooker's family traces its descent. No doubt the two families, the Hookers and Tremaynes knew each other. A seating plan of 1676 from St Ewe, the Tremaynes' local church, shows places reserved both for Balsamus Hooker and Master Hooker close to that occupied by Lewis Tremayne.

Late in his life, Joseph recalled some of his early influences:

> "At the age of five or six my early leaning towards botany was shown by a love of mosses and my mother used to tell an anecdote of me, that, when I was still in petticoats, I was found grubbing in a wall in the dirty suburbs of the dirty city of Glasgow and that, when she asked me what I was about, I cried out that I had found Bryum argenteum......"

Mosses came to hold a fascination for him. He later describes another incident which affected him deeply. It seems that one of his favourite books was *Travels* by Mungo Park and he recalls an incident which occurred when Mungo Park was searching for the source of the Niger, in which he (Mungo Park)

> "became so faint with hunger and fatigue that he laid himself down to die; but being attracted by the brilliant green of a little moss on the bank hard by, said to himself: If God cares for the life of that little moss, He surely will not let me perish in the desert."

Park pocketed a little piece of that moss. Later, a Foulah woman took pity on him; she not only fed him but apparently sang him to sleep as well! A scrap of this moss had been given to Joseph's father, who had in turn, shown it to Joseph. How thrilled the young boy must have been to hear the story and touch that little bit of moss.

His imagination was fired. He goes on to recall his delight, whilst sitting on his grandfather's knee, to hear about the adventures of Captain Cook. His favourite picture was that of:

> "Christmas Harbour ..... with the arched rock standing out to sea and the sailors killing penguins; and I thought that I should be the happiest boy alive if ever I would see that wonderful rock, and knock penguins on the head."

HOOKER'S FIRST VOYAGE

Joseph studied medicine at Glasgow University and his medical qualification enabled him to join the Royal Navy. His first trip was under Captain Ross as assistant doctor and botanist aboard the discovery ship *HMS Erebus*. The *Erebus* and her companion ship *Terror* set out in 1839 on an expedition to pinpoint the magnetic South Pole, a voyage that was to last for four years, during which time Joseph visited Christmas Harbour.

He does not tell us if he knocked penguins on the head or whether it made him *"the happiest boy alive"* if he did, but certainly in 1840 he saw that wonderful arched rock.

EXPEDITION TO INDIA

His second voyage was to India, a choice influenced by his friend Hugh Falconer and supported by his naval boss, Lord Auckland, First Lord of the Admiralty.

Hooker was just 30 when he set off for India in 1847. With no personal fortune, he had a small grant of only £450 per year from the Admiralty; little enough to cover the expenses of such an expedition let alone pay for the many instances of help and hospitality which he received. He was, however, able to reward those whose encouragement and friendship contributed greatly to the success of his travels: he named plants for them.

FRIENDS AND COLLEAGUES

LADY SUSAN DALHOUSIE

One of his first discoveries was the lovely *R. dalhousiae*, which he named for Lady Susan Dalhousie, wife of the Governor General of India in appreciation of his invaluable support. Hooker describes it as:

> *"the most lovely thing you can imagine; a parasite on gigantic trees, three yards high, with whorls of branches and 3-6 immense white, deliciously sweet-scented flowers at the apex of each branch. It is the most splendid thing of its kind I have ever seen and more delicate than the others. ...The odour partakes of that of the lemon. In age the flowers assume a delicate roseate tint...which adds to their beauty."*

He adds that the seed of *R. dalhousiae* was difficult to obtain:

> *"for you cannot see the plant on the limbs of the lofty oaks it inhabits, except it be in flower, and groping at random in the woods is really like digging for daylight....You must remember it is no light work to be the pioneer of these fine things.."*

R. dalhousiae from *Rhododendrons of the Sikkim-Himalaya*

This rhododendron has sad associations; the lovely Lady Susan did not live long to enjoy her namesake: she died from sea sickness during the voyage back to England in 1853.

LORD AUCKLAND, FIRST LORD OF THE ADMIRALTY

The beautiful and fragrant white rhododendron, *R. aucklandii* was named for Lord Auckland in recognition of his support at the beginning of the enterprise:

> *"To this fine plant I have the melancholy satisfaction of affixing the name of the late Right Honourable Lord Auckland, no less in token of my gratitude for the kindness and patronage I received from him when First Lord of the Admiralty, than in memory of his zealous promotion of every scientific inquiry, and his liberal patronage of the arts and sciences while he filled the exalted station of Governor-General of India."*

The name was later changed to *R. griffithianum*, by which it is known today, named for botanist and explorer, William Griffiths.

R. aucklandii
now known as
R. griffithianum from
Rhododendrons of the
Sikkim-Himalaya

DR HUGH FALCONER

Joseph Hooker's great friend, Dr Hugh Falconer, employee of the East India Company and Superintendent first of the Saharanpur Botanical Gardens and later of the Calcutta Botanical Gardens, was remembered in *R. falconeri* and it is a happy chance that one of the most impressive rhododendrons to come from this expedition should have been named after a man with an equally impressive-sounding name. Hooker first came across this species near Darjeeling 1848 as he was trekking through the valley of the Great Rungreet River.

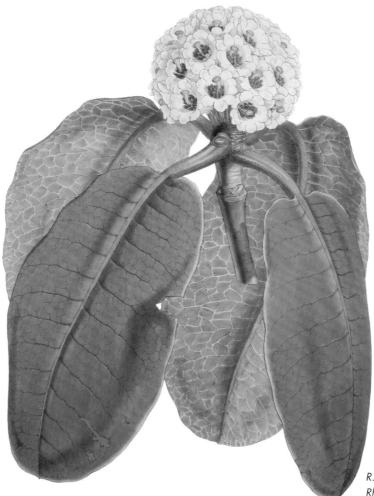

R. falconeri from
*Rhododendrons of
the Sikkim- Himalaya*

BRIAN HODGSON

The greatest influence on the direction of the Indian adventure was Brian Hodgson. He was the British Resident in Darjeeling, a government administrator who used his contacts and his position to smooth Hooker's path. Joseph Hooker stayed with him for some time. Hodgson taught him much about the flora, fauna and customs of India and together they made several expeditions into the hinterland around Darjeeling.

Joseph Hooker acknowledged his help and friendship when he named the mauve *R. hodgsonii* for *"one of my dearest friends on earth"*. He described it as:

"beautiful green with leaves 16 inches long, while the ground was covered with flakes of its bark as delicate as tissue paper and of pale flesh colour."

R. hodgsonii, from
Rhododendrons of
the Sikkim-Himalayas

It was on one of these trips with Brian Hodgson that Hooker found *R. argenteum*, later to be renamed *R. grande*:

> "…*a great tree forty feet high, with magnificent leaves twelve to fifteen inches long, deep green and wrinkled above and silvery below. I know nothing of the kind that exceeds in beauty the flowering branch of R. argenteum, with its wide spreading foliage and glorious mass of flowers.*"

R. argenteum, so named for the silvery underside to the leaves, now known as *R. grande* from *Rhododendrons of the Sikkim-Himalaya*

DR TOMMY THOMPSON

Another of Hooker companions was Dr Tommy Thompson, an old friend who accompanied Hooker on his final expedition in 1849 and then spent much time with him in 1850 arranging and identifying the collection. Hooker acknowledged his help and friendship by naming the deep red *R. thompsonii* for him.

R. thompsonii from *Rhododendrons of the Sikkim-Himalaya*

A RHODODENDRON FOR MRS CAMPBELL

One of Hooker's closest associates was Archibald Campbell. He met him in December 1848 and describes him as *"one who enlightened every enjoyment"*.

They became lifelong friends. In a letter to his father, Sir William, now director of Kew, Hooker says:

> *"I wrote and told him this morning that I would ask you to confirm the name of a Rhododendron on his wife, a little compliment that has touched him to the quick. He is extremely attached to his wife, and I really never saw a man so heartily appreciate a trifling favour."*

The rhododendron he chose was *R. campbelliae*, now considered synonymous with *R. arboreum ssp cinnamomeum*, recognized by the rust-coloured indumentum beneath the leaves and flowers that range from white to a rosy pink.

It was his association with Archibald Campbell that was to bring Hooker into danger. Campbell was a political agent who became involved in Hooker's negotiations with the ruling authorities when he sought permission to travel and to collect plants in Sikkim. The Rajah was, as Hooker put it in one of his letters home to his father, *"very sorry indeed to see us so far into his country"*.

There had been considerable conflict with the British whose interference in affairs had incurred the enmity of the Rajah's chief minister, the Dewan. Hooker and Campbell were attacked and taken prisoner. Hooker describes the attack:

> "He (Campbell) had scarcely left, when I heard him calling loudly to me, Hooker! Hooker! the savages are murdering me!"

The hostility was directed against Campbell who was seized as a political hostage but Hooker was also held prisoner. It was not until five weeks later that a threat from Lord Dalhousie to send in the British troops secured their release.

It must have been a time of great anxiety. Poor Mrs Campbell! She writes:

> "My trial was increased by having to go through my confinement in the midst of it all, but God has been very gracious, I am gaining strength nicely and my baby thrives. I have asked Dr Hooker to be godfather."

He later writes to his mother telling her of this:

> "The new baby is to be named Josephine. It is very small and much the colour of blotting-paper, like all the little babies I ever saw; but some mothers' eyes have a property of neutralizing that tint, as yours must have done, for you say I was a fair and white infant!"

ARCHIBALD CAMPBELL'S MAGNOLIA

The plant that Hooker chose to honour this friend was not a rhododendron but a magnolia. It happened like this. One of Hooker's earliest and most beautiful discoveries was *R. dalhousiae*. This is an epiphyte rhododendron: it grows, not in the ground, but on large trees and the tree on which on which Hooker found it was a magnolia:

> "This superb tree, which forms so conspicuous a feature in the scenery and vegetation of Dorjiling, was chosen by Dr Thomson and myself to commemorate the eminent services of our friend Dr Campbell, Resident at Dorjiling...."

TRIALS AND TRIBULATIONS

The seeds which Hooker collected were hard won. The problems caused by lack of proper funding from home and political obstruction in India were compounded by physical hardship. Many of the areas he explored were mountainous and remote, the climate often harsh. His letters also tell of difficulties dealing with the local people employed as collectors and baggage handlers.

On October 27, 1848 he writes:

"The Bhotan coolies gave me daily trouble from the very commencement up to this hour, they are the most intractable and implacable ruffians, hanged or unhanged, and are utterly useless except they are coldproof".

His philosophy for dealing with them is interesting:

"I have always found frankness and kindness good policy with any nation, especially if combined with a reasonable amount of personal vanity, which I abundantly possess, and assumption of superiority and, above all, a liberally flattering opinion of the people openly expressed."

He adds later that he got the most cooperation when able to convince them that their self-interest coincided with his requirements. While he was being held prisoner, he remarks:

"... as they (his native employees) *will not get a rap of pay until they bring me safe back and what they will receive will be a fortune to each, they will consult their own interests as well as mine."*

Other dangers and discomforts included landslides, leeches and snow blindness (against which Lady Dalhousie had given Hooker one of her veils), together with the risk of injury from the very plants that he had come to collect. Hooker records that some rhododendron wood (probably *R. cinnabarinum*):

"...when used as a fuel causes the face to swell and the eyes to inflame".

UNFAMILIAR FOOD BROUGHT ITS OWN PROBLEMS

"A little yak milk was all I could procure here; and as a case containing 8lb of what I had supposed to be preserved meat, proved to be only prunes, I was obliged to be very strictly careful over our provisioning."

The terrain was rough and collecting seeds was at times fraught with hazard. Some of these adventures he shared with his puppy Kinchin, a Tibetan mastiff, who he describes as:

"... huge, grave and bull-headed ...his glorious bushy tail over his back in a majestic sweep, and a thick collar of scarlet wool round his neck and shoulders, setting off his long silky coat to the best advantage."

He recalls that:

"Avalanches of stones are dreadfully numerous and dangerous. Kinchin has had his whiskers actually shaved on one side by a great rolling stone."

Kinchin's luck did not hold out. He slipped off a narrow bridge and was lost in the turbulent waters beneath.

SEEDS OF SUCCESS

It had been an incredible three years. Hooker had endured real hardship and privation. He had shared meals with rats and cockroaches. He had ridden elephants, been soaked by the rain and blinded by the snow. He had been immortalised on the walls of a Changachelling temple in a flowered coat, tartar cap and shoes with turned-up toes and he had collected great quantities of rhododendron seed, seed that is as fine as dust, and this he sent back to Kew. Each delivery of seeds was meticulously recorded in the Goods Inward Book. It must have been an exciting time for Sir William, unpacking the boxes, opening the small calico bags, to see what his son had sent him!

Some of the seeds were retained at Kew to be germinated. Many more were distributed to friends, to sponsors, to nurseries, to botanical gardens and institutes, both at home and overseas and it was this widespread distribution which had such a dramatic effect on English horticulture. Within only a few years rhododendrons, from being almost unknown, became available to every English gardener.

THE PIONEER OF THESE FINE THINGS

Joseph Hooker brought rhododendrons into prominence in a spectacular fashion. Their popularity increased, exceeding that of any group of plants in history. It was said that:

"The money spent on rhododendrons during twenty years in this country would nearly suffice to pay off the National Debt."

(Shirley Hibbert 1871)

SEEDS COME TO HELIGAN

Heligan did not receive seeds or seedlings directly from Kew but from Sir Charles Lemon of Carclew, one of Joseph Hooker's friends and sponsors, and to whom the Tremayne family was closely related by marriage. It was from these seeds that Heligan's fine Indian rhododendrons were grown.

The new rhododendrons fuelled a mania for hybridizing and hundreds of hybrids were bred for the English climate: it is these original species and the hybrids that were developed from them that form the main part of the rhododendron Collection at Heligan.

RHODODENDRON HYBRIDS

The great Cornish horticulturist, J C Williams once said:

> *"Start hybridizing …….. It's the greatest fun. You get ten, fifteen, perhaps even twenty years of pleasurable anticipation, and only one day of disappointment – the day your seedlings open their first flowers!"*
>
> (J C Williams to Collingwood Ingram RYB 1967)

Rhododendrons are an hybridizer's dream. The pollen grains are similar in size and shape, allowing different species easily to cross with each other to produce a wide range of variations. These show the combined characteristics of the parents and, as in every species, some make better parents than others.

The first species used in hybridizing were *R. arboreum* and *R. ponticum*, together with the American *R. catawbience*. Crosses were made in the 1830s and the cultivars *R.* 'Russellianum' and *R.* 'Smithii' resulted from these early experiments.

The hybrid *R.* 'Cornish Early Red' was probably developed at the Randall Nursery in St Austell, which, according to Cornish horticulturalist, Walter Magor, was likely to have been the source of many of these popular hybrids in Cornwall.

Experiments in hybridizing were not confined to nurseries: many private individuals, including the Tremaynes, tried their hand.

John Tremayne is credited with making the first cross between the blood-red *R. arboreum* and *R. griffithianum*, a Hooker introduction that was highly valued as a parent. According to the *Gardeners' Chronicle* of 1896, Heligan had a very good form of this: *"pinker than is usual with this species"*. The resulting hybrid *R.* 'John Tremayne' was registered as a named cultivar, although some sources (Lionel de Rothschild) say that it was created by his son Jack:

> *"Captain Tremayne of Heligan crossed blood red R. arboreum with R. griffithianum to produce 'John Tremayne' and 'Mrs Babington".*

There are many *R. arboreum* x
R. griffithianum hybrids at Heligan. They
vary enormously. Some are quite small
with a low scrambling habit and a
delicate green spotting to the throat:
others are huge, amongst the tallest in the
garden. Some have rather poor, plain and
sparse flowers, not a plant you would buy
if given a choice: others are a strong pink,
frilled and shapely. The bark of some of
these rhododendrons is particularly
attractive with delicate flakes of soft pink
and pale cinnamon.

R. griffithianum hybrid

Perhaps it was either John or Jack
Tremayne who raised these plants, from
the same seed grex that produced R. 'John
Tremayne'. Alternatively, these plants could have come from Richard Gill's nursery at
Tremough. In one of his catalogues Gill offers for sale:

> *"Aucklandii* (syn griffithianum) *Crosses Unnamed. A series of crosses with
> that fine species as parent. Most of the plants have large foliage and are all
> strong growers. From 10/6."*

THE LATER RHODODENDRON SPECIES

While Hooker collected in India, other plant-hunters, Robert Fortune, Augustine Henry
together with a group of courageous French missionaries, were beginning to rifle the
botanical treasure chest of China. Plant-hunting became increasingly a commercial
activity, financed by the lucrative nursery trade.

It was a gloriously exciting time to be a nurseryman. China, her borders prised open
by the Opium Wars, was proving to be rich beyond measure and new species were being
introduced in their thousands; not only from China but also from Japan and other areas
of the Far East. Some of these new introductions fetched huge sums: there are stories of
rare orchids fetching 1000 guineas.

One of the most successful nurseries in this period was James Veitch & Sons. John
Veitch opened his first nursery in Devon in 1808, and in 1832 established the famous
Exeter nursery. It was very much a family business, involving both his son and his
grandsons. It was one of these grandsons, James, who was sent up to London to train
with two of the great nurseries of the day, Chandler & Booth in Vauxhall and William
Rollisson & Sons of Tooting. James realized that Devon was too far away to compete
with the London nurseries and in 1850 he established the London business on the
premises of Knight & Perry's Royal Exotic Nursery in the Kings Road.

By the time Harry, his son, took over in the 1880s, the Veitch dynasty was approaching its pomp. Two of its early great collectors were Cornishmen Thomas and William Lobb from Pencarrow, close to Heligan, followed later by one of the most famous plant-hunters, Ernest Wilson.

E H WILSON

'Chinese' Wilson was 23 when he set out for China, charged by Harry Veitch with finding that most beautiful of trees, *Davidia involucrata*, a single specimen of which had been located by amateur botanist Augustine Henry. Wilson left England in 1900, sailing to San Francisco and then on to China, his only guide a rough sketch map of 20,000 square miles of country, with the location of the precious tree marked with a cross. Extraordinary though it may sound, Wilson found the actual location. To his

Davidia involucrata

chagrin, however, he saw not the flourishing tree of his dreams, but a freshly sawn-off stump and next to it a new house, with splendid roof timbers! His diary noted, with commendable restraint:

"I did not sleep during the night of April 25th 1900."

Davidia involucrata had been found several years earlier by the great French botanist Père Paul Farges, a Roman Catholic missionary who spent many years in western China searching for souls and botanical delights but Wilson was the first to introduce it into the UK.

Several years after his last expedition for Veitch in 1903, the Coombe Wood nursery was sold up and a huge clearance sale took place. This was in 1914. There is no record of Jack Tremayne attending this sale but Heligan has several plants that could well have come from there: *Davidia involucrata* in the Sundial Garden, *Camellia cuspidata* on Beacon Path, *R. ririei* on Dovecote Lawn and *R. lutescens* close to the Bee Boles.

Wilson made six trips to China, three for Veitch and three for The Arnold Arboretum in Washington, expeditions full of adventure and danger. He died in a car crash in America in 1930 having brought 250 new species and ten new genera to the outside world.

GEORGE FORREST

Contemporary with E H Wilson was the Scotsman George Forrest. He was born just three years before Wilson, and spent twenty-eight years collecting plants in western

China. He was a tough man. He used a small inheritance to seek his fortune in Australia, first as a gold prospector and then as a sheep farmer. These early experiences were to stand him in good stead.

He began his plant-hunting career working for A K Bulley, proprietor of Bees Seeds, but later was sponsored by syndicates whose leader was J C Williams of Caerhays. In his seven expeditions to China he faced rigours and dangers as great as any of his courageous predecessors. During a period of intense political unrest he escaped a violent band of Tibetans, his hat pierced by poisoned arrows, only to step on a fire-hardened bamboo spike that resulted in a foot so severely infected that he was always afterwards to walk with a limp. Forced to disguise himself and go into hiding, he was assumed to be dead and his family informed. His dearly-loved wife Clem mourned for a week before he was able to gets news to her that he had survived.

His was lucky: his companions Father Daberand and Father Bourdonnec were hideously tortured and killed by the rebels.

Forrest is responsible for Heligan's most recent rhododendron species introductions: *R. sinogrande*, which he first came across in 1912 on the Salween Divide, and *R. griersonianum*, introduced in 1917. In previous syndicate-sponsored expeditions, the seeds collected were distributed between the members of the syndicate. For the 1917-1919 trip, J C Williams put a lien on all rhododendron seeds, so that Caerhays alone received the lovely *R. griersonianum*, named for R C Grierson of the Yunnan Customs Service.

One rhododendron at Heligan presents a puzzle, *R. decorum*. This Chinese rhododendron was first described by French botanist Franchet in 1887. E H Wilson brought it to the UK and it appeared in the Veitch catalogue for 1900 (price 7/6d and 10/-) but it was listed under the Himalayan Rhododendrons section. However, the Cornish botanist, Frederick Hamilton Davey, noted in his article, *The Acclimatization of Exotics in Cornwall*, that Heligan has this species growing in the garden. The article was written in 1897 and the plant must already have been large enough to be noteworthy which implies an earlier introduction but I can find no record of it.

Rhododendrons from the later explorations of George Forrest in China never arrived at Heligan. The result is that the rhododendrons in the Collection represent what was available and popular during the Victorian period and early 20th century, giving a rare opportunity to experience a garden planted as it was an hundred years ago.

John Tremayne died in 1901. He had been squire for almost the whole of Queen Victoria's extraordinary reign. He had inherited Heligan in 1851, the year of the Great Exhibition held in Hyde Park whose jewel was the Crystal Palace and whose purpose was to show the world that Britain was great, powerful and, thanks to her position as *"the workshop of the world"* (David Chambers), very rich. Under John's guidance and with later contributions from Jack, Heligan evolved from a garden laid out in good English taste, with grass walks and beautiful vistas, to a woodland garden of rides and glades, of shaded walks and sunlit lawns; secret grottos and deep paths through steep and rocky valleys, all planted with the treasures of five continents. It is in this setting that Heligan's rhododendron Collection is displayed.

7
RHODODENDRON TOUR OF THE NORTHERN GARDENS

The rhododendron Collection it is one of the essential elements of Heligan's appeal. It is extraordinary, not for the number of different varieties that it contains, but for the sheer size and magnificence of its specimens together with the manner in which they are displayed. They are planted, not as a way of exhibiting individual specimens but as an integral part of the design of the garden. Plants are grouped in naturalistic settings, in woodland walks, shrubberies, or forest glades so that they can be admired individually but also contribute to an overall effect that exceeds the sum of its parts.

There are over 300 rhododendrons in the garden; far too many to refer to individually, so most will be described in their settings while plants of particular interest will be noted.

Heligan's rhododendrons are the living structure of the gardens. In the Northern Gardens, they encircle Flora's Green, defining the shape of this open grassy centerpiece.

R. 'Cornish Red' hybrids on Flora's Green

RHODODENDRON TOUR OF
THE NORTHERN GARDENS

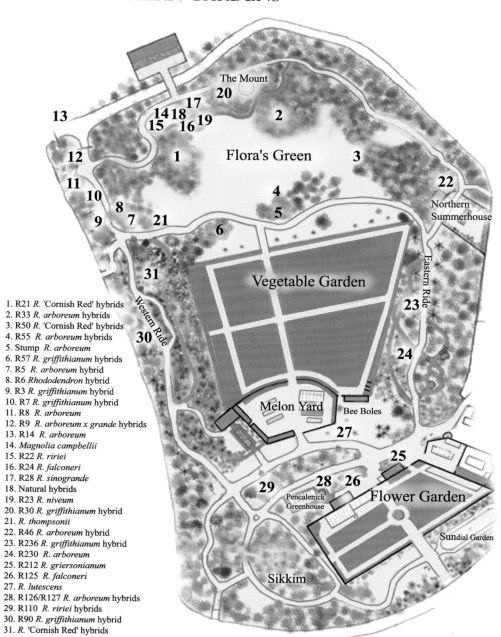

1. R21 *R.* 'Cornish Red' hybrids
2. R33 *R. arboreum* hybrids
3. R50 *R.* 'Cornish Red' hybrids
4. R55 *R. arboreum* hybrids
5. Stump *R. arboreum*
6. R57 *R. griffithianum* hybrids
7. R5 *R. arboreum* hybrid
8. R6 *Rhododendron* hybrid
9. R3 *R. griffithianum* hybrid
10. R7 *R. griffithianum* hybrid
11. R8 *R. arboreum*
12. R9 *R. arboreum x grande* hybrids
13. R14 *R. arboreum*
14. *Magnolia campbellii*
15. R22 *R. ririei*
16. R24 *R. falconeri*
17. R28 *R. sinogrande*
18. Natural hybrids
19. R23 *R. niveum*
20. R30 *R. griffithianum* hybrid
21. *R. thompsonii*
22. R46 *R. arboreum* hybrid
23. R236 *R. griffithianum* hybrid
24. R230 *R. arboreum*
25. R212 *R. griersonianum*
26. R125 *R. falconeri*
27. *R. lutescens*
28. R126/R127 *R. arboreum* hybrids
29. R110 *R. ririei* hybrids
30. R90 *R. griffithianum* hybrid
31. *R.* 'Cornish Red' hybrids

They form huge billowing masses, the sinuous, rich brown limbs layering themselves into the ground, rooting where they touch the earth. They form a backbone to the Rides, punctuating the borders, rising to a height of twelve metres, silhouetting their blooms against the sky. These are giants amongst rhododendrons, reputedly amongst the largest in the country.

For most of the year they provide a lush green backcloth that acts as a foil to other flowering plants. Then in March, for two short months, the rhododendrons at Heligan burst into glowing glory with an exuberance that would overpower a less magnificent setting.

The potential of these plants to produce large masses of bold colour very much influenced ideas of garden design in the 19th century and, when Heligan's rhododendrons were planted, it had become the fashion to use solid blocks of colour to give a rich and dramatic look to garden features that sought to replicate the foreign landscapes of woodland walks and open glades from which the plants originated. This style of planting was used to great effect at Heligan to give one of the most impressive floral displays you will ever see.

The tour begins on Flora's Green. It is surrounded by great mounds of rhododendrons, heaped piles of glowing colour, set off by the smooth green grass. Flowers begin to appear in February and these early blossoms sound the first notes of a melody that will ripple around Flora's Green, reaching a crescendo as the huge clumps come into full flower.

As you face north, the large mound to the left, R21, is composed of two groups of plants, slightly different in colour. The massive pile to the east, R50, is a deep magenta. These are R. 'Cornish Red' hybrids, produced by crossing the tree-like R. *arboreum* with the purple R. *ponticum*.

The centre group, R33 a much paler pink, are R. *arboreum* hybrids.

R21 R. 'Cornish Red' hybrids on Flora's Green   R33 R. *arboreum* hybrids on Flora's Green

There is some evidence that these rhododendrons originally formed part of a mixed woodland planting: there a few surviving trees of holly and bay within the groups, but over the years the vigour of the ponticum element has caused the rhododendrons to spread out, smothering other plants.

On the south side of Flora's Green is a group of deep red hybrids, produced by crossing the evocatively named blood-red *R. arboreum* with *R. griffithianum*. Where these crosses were made and by whom is not known, although there is some archival evidence to suggest that Jack Tremayne raised them in the early 20th century: certainly they look to be younger than the other hybrids on the Green.

R55 Blood-red hybrids on the south side of Flora's Green

Close to the entrance to the Vegetable Garden there is a massive stump, the remains of what was the most magnificent red *R. arboreum*, R56, possibly dating from the original introduction of the species. The tree had been dying for several years, finally succumbing in 2008.

On the other side of the path is a group of *R. griffithianum* hybrids, distinguished from the many other *R. griffithianum* hybrids in the gardens by heavy green spotting on the centre lobe. Remedial pruning has recently been carried out on this group.

Massive stump of *R. arboreum* on Flora's Green

As you leave Flora's Green and go up Western Ride, the borders are studded with rhododendrons, both species and hybrids.

R5 is a deep pink *R. arboreum* hybrid, showing many characteristics of a true arboreum but lacking the coloured indumentum on the undersides of its leaves.

R57 *R. griffithianum* hybrids on Flora's Green

R5 *R. arboreum* hybrid, Western Ride

Beside this is a low-growing hybrid, one of the earliest to bloom, the pale pink flowers with their long pink stamens are a great attraction for the early bees.

On the other side of the path is R3, one of the many May-flowering *R. griffithianum* hybrids in the garden. Some of these hybrids are planted in large groups, composed of plants of exactly the same type, ie clones: others are planted as single trees and vary greatly in their size and habit. The clones were probably brought in from a nursery. All have great pyramidal pink trusses, often faintly scented, that bring vibrant colour to the late spring garden.

R3 is now almost prostrate, its root ball torn from the ground. It must once have been a huge tree, outgrowing the protection of the laurel shelterbelt on the outside of the Ride.

R6 Low-growing hybrid on Western Ride

R3 *R. griffithianum* hybrid on Western Ride

In this area there are several other hybrids, R7, R17, R18 and R20, their huge orangey-pink florets indicating their *R. griffithianum* parentage.

R7 Deep pink *R. griffithianum* hybrid on Western Ride

Close to the top of Western ride is R8, one of the most important rhododendrons in the garden, a deep pink *R. arboreum*, one of the original Hooker introductions and a mighty tree over 12 metres tall.

R8 original Hooker *R. arboreum*

At the top of Western Ride, to the right is a group of R. 'Cornish Red' hybrids and to the left, R9 and R10 two rhododendrons that posed a puzzle. They are quite small trees, only about 6 metres high, rather open and rangy, the leaves and flowers similar to R. grande. The buds are bright pink, gradually fading as the florets fully open, their voluptuous stigmas waiting to kiss the pollen from marauding bees.

These trees were identified by the late Edward Needham, a noted rhododendron expert and modern day plant-hunter, as R. arboreum x R. grande hybrids.

Behind these two, visible over the green gates, is another of the Hooker originals, R14, a deep red R. arboreum known as The Poodle.

R9 R. arboreum x R. grande hybrid

R14 original Hooker R. arboreum

Magnolia campbellii on Dovecote Lawn

The path now leads to Dovecote lawn, to one of the inspired plantings at Heligan. The centerpiece is the magnificent Magnolia campbellii, named by Joseph Hooker for his friend and fellow captive, Archibald Campbell, its huge pink goblets visible from the coast at Mevagissy, and beneath, a group of the lovely R. ririei, R22.

R. ririei is a small tree, growing only to about four metres, the angular grace of its slim trunks reminiscent of a Chinese painting. Its leaves are of soft green, with silvery undersides and its flowers, which are carried in flat trusses, are deep mauve with black nectar pouches. It blooms early, in January, sometimes even in December.

In a mild winter, the sight of this delicate rhododendron in flower is the prerogative of the gardeners and the hardiest of visitors: a cold winter will delay flowering so that these two plants flower in unison, the purple of the *R. ririei* trusses set against the deep pink magnolia buds.

R. *ririei* was discovered by E H Wilson on Mt Omei in Sichuan and collected for the Veitch nursery in 1904. Wilson named it for his friend Reverend B Ririe.

As you go east along Beacon Path, treasures follow in quick succession. On the right there is a grassy glade, encircled by five rhododendrons.

R22 Winter-flowering *R. ririei*

R24, *R. falconeri*, is one of Hooker's original introductions, firm, cool, creamy-white globes contrasting with the deep gingery indumentum on the undersides of its leaves.

Next to it is R28 *R. sinogrande*, one of George Forrest's discoveries, introduced in 1912.

R24 *R. falconeri*, on Beacon Path

R28 *R. sinogrande* on Beacon Path

These two rhododendrons have a close and productive relationship, freely exchanging their pollen and giving rise to many self-set hybrids, each unique, each showing in various degrees the characteristics of its parents.

Natural hybrids produced by cross-pollination between *R. sinogrande* and *R. falconeri*.

Behind these two, on the edge of Flora's Green, is R23 *R. niveum*, so called because of the whitish felted indumentum on the undersides of its leaves. This is probably one of the largest original Hooker *R. niveum* plants left in existence. Heligan is fortunate that it is still here and for a strange reason.

For a while, *R. niveum* enjoyed great popularity and was widely planted in Victorian gardens. The species then lost favour: many were uprooted and consigned to the bonfire.

So why this sudden demise, this relegation to the compost heap? Blame Hargreaves and his spinning jenny. Machines such as these enabled the

R23 Massed blooms of the much-maligned *R. niveum* on Flora's Green

abundant supply of cheap raw material from India and America to be manufactured into inexpensive cotton cloth. Cheap material required cheap dyes and the Victorian version of Tyrian purple that proved so successful was the accidental result of a chemical experiment performed by the young William Perkins in 1837. The resulting aniline dye produced a purple colour called mauveine. This was very popular for a number of years, so much so that Queen Victoria wore a silk gown dyed this colour to the Royal Exhibition in 1862 but by the end of the 1860s the colour had become unfashionable. It had become associated with the cotton material used for the uniforms of domestic staff and hospital nursing assistants and these associations became distasteful to the leisured and affluent owners of Victorian pleasure gardens.

There is another explanation. When seen on its own as a specimen tree, the mauve of the flowers make a pleasing contrast with the white felted leaves, but used as part of a planned colour scheme it is easy to see that it might not have worked well. The tree at Heligan is a better shade than some, but even so it can look decidedly ashy on a dull and misty Cornish day. The use of colour in garden design was becoming more sophisticated, soon to reach new heights in the work of Gertrude Jekyll, so that it was more likely to have been aesthetics rather than social snobbery which resulted in the removal of so many *R. niveum* in the latter years of Victoria's reign.

Why was the one at Heligan spared? Was John Tremayne more egalitarian than many of his counterparts, or less concerned with considerations of colour? Certainly he was a plantsman, an enthusiastic collector of new plants which were pouring into England from all parts of the expanding Victorian world. No doubt it would have been a source of great satisfaction to possess a plant from the first introduction of the particular species, a satisfaction more important than class sensibilities or aesthetic considerations of colour. Whatever the explanation, the *R. niveum* at Heligan is a rarity.

Close to the path on the right is a pink *R. arboreum*, and next to it, one of the most beautiful rhododendrons in the garden. R30 is a hybrid, with *R. griffithianum* and *R. fortunei* in its parentage. Its florets, rosy in bud, open into trumpets of palest pink, sweetly scented. Nothing is known of its provenance: Richard Gill of Tremough was producing hybrids of this type and, like several other rhododendrons in the garden, it may well have come from the Tremough nursery.

R30 *R. griffithianum* hybrid

Along the left-hand side of Beacon Path, inside the boundary wall, there are a number of large laurels, part of the original planting designed to protect the gardens from the cold, drying easterly winds. The laurels were interspersed with *R. ponticum*, a much-valued plant during the 19th century. At Heligan, *R. ponticum* was used as a colourful and effective windbreak both in the Northern Gardens and in the Jungle. Now, specifically targeted as disease carriers, these plants have been removed and with them part of Heligan's horticultural heritage.

As you follow Beacon Path towards the Northern Summerhouse garden, there are hybrids on both sides and amongst this planting is just one species rhododendron, R40, *R. thompsonii*. This is one of Hooker's introductions and this plant dates from the 1850s.

W. Roberts, writing in the *Gardeners' Chronicle* in 1896, tells us that this tree is:

> *"quite 25 feet high, and is probably the largest of this species in England."*

Sadly it is now almost dead, just a single thin trunk arching over the path to mark its position. Attempts at propagating from it have not been successful but there are some young plants of *R. thompsonii* on the south side of Flora's Green.

New plant of *R. thompsonii* on Flora's Green

R46 *R. griffithianum* hybrid in the
Northern Summerhouse garden

From here, the walk takes you into the
Northern Summerhouse garden where a
May-flowering *R. griffithianum* hybrid
prettily frames the little summerhouse, the
oldest structure in the garden.

From here, go south down Eastern
Ride. On the right is a very attractive
hybrid, R236, with delicate fluted edges
to its petals. Its provenance is not known:
it may have been raised at Heligan or
purchased from the Richard Gill nursery
at Tremough.

R236 *R. griffithianum* hybrid

Further down the Eastern Ride, on the
right, is R230, the last remnant of the only
Hooker blood-red *R. arboreum* left in the
garden. The dark red variety grows
naturally at the lower altitudes of the
Himalayas and is less hardy than the
paler-coloured varieties.

On the left is a fine group of
R. arboreum hybrids surrounding the
Grotto and a huge deep pink *R. arboreum*,
R219, at the bottom of the Ride.

R230 Blood-red *R. arboreum*

As you turn right towards the Flower Garden, there is a group of low-growing rhododendrons, straggly, their brittle, fragile branches hung with lichen, growing in what was the nursery area of the garden. These are the summer-flowering *R. griersonianum*, introduced by George Forrest in 1917 for J C Williams at Caerhays. The Heligan plants may well have came as seedlings directly from Caerhays. They were heeled in, but by this time Jack, the last squire at Heligan, was preparing to leave for good to go and live in Italy and these vibrant geranium-red rhododendrons were never planted out in the main garden.

R212 *R. griersonianum*

At the entrance to the Flower Garden, overhanging the Head Gardener's Office, stands one of the finest rhododendrons in the garden, R125 *R. falconeri*.

Hooker first came across this species near Darjeeling in 1848. As you stand beneath this enormous tree you can imagine his wonder on seeing it for the first time. This species is beautiful on so many counts. First you see its smooth, sinuous limbs, deep mahogany dappled with darker patches and, where the bark is sheltered, the outer layers peel off in milk chocolate curls. Follow the bare branches snaking up into the foliage and you see the underside of the leaves, a deep rich gingery colour, velvety to the touch. The true glory comes in April when this magnificent old rhododendron is covered by several hundred huge flower heads, great candelabra of palest cream flowers, each truss the size of a melon. In 1896 this tree is recorded as bearing 258 trusses, one of which was 36 inches in circumference.

Peer up into the waxy bells and see the deep purple flashes inside, a colour described by Hooker as 'blood-purple'.

R125 *R. falconeri*
flower showing
the deep purple
nectar pouch

This tree is over 12 metres high and spreads as wide. It is amongst the oldest in England and has been here for over a 150 years, grown from a seed no bigger than a speck of dust.

In recent years the tree's condition had deteriorated. The soil level around its base had gradually sunk, leaving the roots bare and exposed; the leaves were undersized and ragged, their indumentum patchy and there were few flowers. A low stone wall was built around the tree, the soil replaced and the surface kept well-mulched. A gradual improvement has taken place

R125 The great *R. falconeri* outside the Head Gardener's office

and now the tree is once again a magnificent sight.

There are seven old *R. falconeri* the garden, an eighth was lost just a couple of years ago. This is a timely reminder that these trees are old, their longevity is uncertain because they are already amongst the oldest in the country and so there is no experience to indicate their expected lifespan in the Cornish climate. They need to be cared for if they are to continue to grace the garden and delight those who come to see them.

Look to the north of the *R. falconeri* and on the Bee Boles lawn is a pretty little rhododendron, *R. lutescens*, planted close to the entrance to the Melon Yard. This is one of E H Wilson's most attractive rhododendron introductions, its soft yellow flowers held in delicate loose trusses, catching the spring sunshine.

The area around the Pencalenick greenhouse is planted with a medley of *R. arboreum* hybrids.

R. lutescens on the Bee Boles Lawn

R126 and R127, Pencalenick greenhouse

Earliest to flower in February are what appear to be *R. ririei* hybrids while pink *R. griffithianum* hybrids extend the season of colour into May.

From here the path leads towards Sikkim, so called after the region of India where Joseph Hooker made many of his discoveries. This part of the garden is planted with a mixture of *R. arboreum* hybrids, including a fine white variety, R48, together with several species rhododendrons, including *R. grande*, *R. falconeri* and a beautiful specimen of the 1912 Forrest introduction *R. sinogrande*, whose huge flowers hang over the path.

R110 *R. ririei* hybrids, Pencalenick greenhouse

Rhododendrons from Sikkim

Here too is *R. decorum*, R132, whose presence in the garden several years before its recorded introduction into the country remains unexplained.

It is difficult to imagine what these areas looked like when they were first laid out, well over a hundred years ago. Surely the men that planted these rhododendrons would be astonished by the grand tapestry of colour and form.

The final part of the Northern Gardens tour takes you north up the Western Ride towards the garden entrance, with a selection of hybrids interspersed with the many camellias along the Ride.

R85 is a deep pink *R. arboreum* hybrid with gingery indumentum: R94 an *R. arboreum* hybrid raised from one of the original 'blood red' varieties: R73 a May-flowering pink *R. griffithianum* hybrid.

R90 has a sweetly-scented white flower, again an *R. griffithianum* hybrid, and on the left along the ridge of the Ravine there is a grove of *R.* 'Cornish Red' hybrids.

As you return to Flora's Green, look back towards the south, to Pencalenick and Sikkim, for it is from a distance that these rhododendrons are best seen, a sea of colour; waves of bright pinks, deep reds and the odd spume of white, washing over the tops of the trees.

R90 sweet-scented *R. griffithianum* hybrid

8

RHODODENDRON TOUR OF THE JUNGLE

A deep, steep-sided valley falls away south from Heligan House towards the sea at Pentewan. Descend into the Jungle and you enter a world set apart, drawn into the unique atmosphere created by its pools and cascades, its dense and lush planting, the familiar and the exotic merging to magical effect.

The creation of this most spectacular of Cornish valley gardens is a masterpiece of imagination and inspiration. In early times the upper part of the valley was an orchard and vegetable garden. It was Squire John who began developing the existing pond and watercourse into a series of linked pools and who planted the great trees for which men risked, and sometimes gave, their lives to bring back from overseas. Tree ferns (*Dicksonia antarctica*) flourish here, brought over originally from Australia as ballast for ships docking in nearby Mevagissy, together with Chusan palms (*Trachycarpus fortunei*), the monstrous giant rhubarb (*Gunnera manicata*), Skunk Cabbage from America (*Lysichiton americanus*) and Jack Treymayne's passion, bamboo, the many different species adding a delicate fluidity to the kaleidoscope of colour and texture.

It is amongst this luxuriant vegetation that the rhododendrons are planted, almost all hybrids, to produce a breathtaking array of form and colour.

Exotic planting
in the Jungle

RHODODENDRON TOUR OF THE JUNGLE

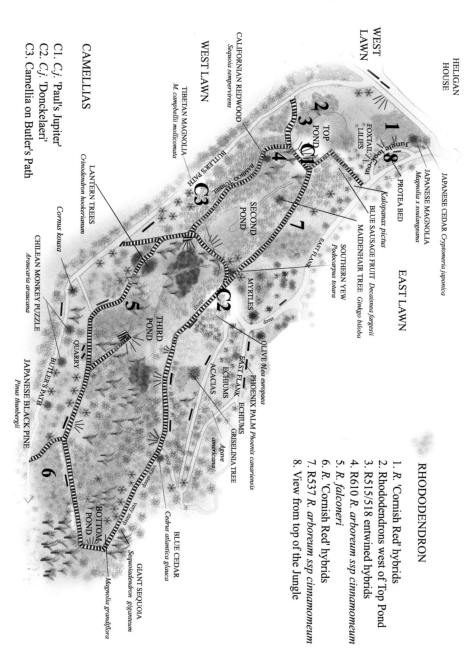

HELIGAN HOUSE

WEST LAWN

JAPANESE CEDAR *Cryptomeria japonica*

JAPANESE MAGNOLIA *Magnolia x soulangeana*

PROTEA BED

Kalopanax pictus

BLUE SAUSAGE FRUIT *Decaisnea fargesii*

MAIDENHAIR TREE *Ginkgo biloba*

SOUTHERN YEW *Podocarpus totara*

FOXTAIL LILIES

TOP POND

SECOND POND

BAMBOO TUNNEL

BUTLER'S PATH

EAST FLANK

MYRTLES

EAST LAWN

WEST LAWN

CALIFORNIAN REDWOOD *Sequoia sempervirens*

TIBETAN MAGNOLIA *M. campbellii mollicomata*

LANTERN TREES *Crinodendron hookerianum*

Cornus kousa

CHILEAN MONKEY PUZZLE *Araucaria araucana*

JAPANESE BLACK PINE *Pinus thunbergii*

THIRD POND

QUARRY

BUTLER'S PATH

BOTTOM POND

OLIVE *Olea europaea*

EAST FLANK

ECHIUMS

ECHIUMS

ACACIAS

Agave americana

GRISELINIA TREE

PHOENIX PALM *Phoenix canariensis*

BLUE CEDAR *Cedrus atlantica glauca*

GIANT SEQUOIA *Sequoiadendron giganteum*

Magnolia grandiflora

CAMELLIAS

C1. *C.j.* 'Paul's Jupiter'
C2. *C.j.* 'Donckelaeri'
C3. Camelia on Butler's Path

RHODODENDRON

1. *R.* 'Cornish Red' hybrids
2. Rhododendrons west of Top Pond
3. R515/518 entwined hybrids
4. R610 *R. arboreum ssp cinnamomeum*
5. *R. falconeri*
6. *R.* 'Cornish Red' hybrids
7. R537 *R. arboreum ssp cinnamomeum*
8. View from top of the Jungle

It is extraordinary to remember that this was achieved by a man who had never seen these plants in maturity: these were new creations whose eventual size and shape was unknown: we are so privileged to see what Squire John could barely have imagined – the planted valley in its pomp.

R. 'Cornish Red' hybrids above Top Pond

The walk begins at the head of the valley. There are over one hundred old rhododendrons in the Jungle. The display begins early, sometimes as early as February, as the first sugar-pink rhododendron opens on the East Flank followed swiftly by three mighty magenta *R.* 'Cornish Red' hybrids on the banks of Top Pond.

In March the colour moves further down the valley until in April the whole of the West Flank is a mass of brilliant flowers.

Rhododendrons west of Top Pond

To the west of Top Pond is a magnificent stand of mixed *R. arboreum* and *R. arboreum* hybrids, every shade from white to deep red, including the curious R515/R518, that bears flowers of red and white seemingly on the same tree which in reality is two trees, planted together and now inextricably entwined. Arching limbs stretch out over the water, reflected in its quiet surface.

Rhododendrons reflected in Top Pond

Beneath the bridge below Top Pond is a pretty *R. arboreum ssp cinnamomeum*, R610, pale pink flowers contrasting with the deep rust-coloured indumentum beneath its leaves.

R610 *R. arboreum ssp cinnamomeum*

Follow the boardwalk to the viewing
platform by Bamboo Pond and from this
vantage point you can see the valley
floor studded with groups of
rhododendron hybrids.

One lone *R. falconeri* overlooks the
valley below Second Pond, best seen from
the viewing platform by Third Pond.

There are very few species
rhododendrons in the Jungle, perhaps
the damper, more humid conditions suit
them less than the airy upland of the
Northern Gardens.

Towards the bottom of the valley is a
huge group of *R.* 'Cornish Red' hybrids,
covering the hillside from Butler's Path
down to the water's edge at Bottom Pond.

These hybrids have developed a
sprawling habit, clinging to the steep sides,
covering the slopes with deep green shiny
foliage that in April become a glowing sea
of colour. Look into these great clumps
and wonder at the writhing mass of limbs
which have quietly, inexorably, claimed
the hillside over the past 150 years.

Sculptural limbs of *R.* 'Cornish Red' hybrids
above Bottom Pond

Rhododendron hybrids in the Jungle

R. falconeri below Second Pond

From the bottom of the valley, you begin the steep climb up East Flank, There are fewer rhododendrons planted on this side, but from here you can fully appreciate the grandeur of the rhododendrons on the other bank.

Here on the East Flank, close to the boardwalk leading up to Top Pond, you can see the remnants of what must have been one of the finest rhododendrons in the whole garden. This is R537, *R. arboreum ssp cinnamomeum*, the undersides of its leaves furred with rust-coloured indumentum, its flowers pure white with deep purple spotting in the throat.

The final climb to the top of the boardwalk rewards you with the stunning panorama of the rhododendrons down the length of the valley.

The lifespan of rhododendrons in the Cornish climate is not known. Species rhododendrons such as *R. griffithianum*, *R. thompsonii*, *R. wightii*, *R. dalhousiae* and *R. hodgsonii*, known to have been here in the garden, have not survived although whether they have died through damage, disease or natural senescence is not known.

What is clear is that action needs to be taken now to preserve what remains by careful management and to conserve the genetic material by propagating from these survivors to delight future generations.

R. 'Cornish Red' hybrids from East Flank

R537 R. arboreum ssp cinnamomeum

Rhododendrons on East Flank in the Jungle

CREATING A FUTURE HISTORY

In the spring of 2003 Heligan seemed enchanted. Thousands of people had followed the reclaiming and restoration of the garden through the writings of Tim Smit, the inspiration and dynamo of the undertaking. Many more were captivated, following the progress of the restoration through a series of television programmes, sharing the excitement, the discoveries, the set-backs and the achievements of those early years, those years of work and vision that were now culminating in glorious re-emergence.

The story of Heligan is the story of the botanical exploration of the world written in roots and branches, but it is a garden, a place of living things that follow their own life cycles, short or long, and because these plants are not growing in their natural habitat, their lifespan is not easy to assess.

RHODODENDRON CONSERVATION

Heligan's rhododendrons are vulnerable. Since 2002 Heligan has lost at least 27. In 2006 a magnificent pink *R. arboreum* suddenly fell across the Western Ride one Saturday morning: another at the entrance to the Northern Gardens died on its feet and in 2008 a great *R. arboreum* fell across the drive, missing the Post Office van by minutes.

One of the old labels unearthed bears witness to the fact that *R. campylocarpum* once grew here.

The pink-budded *R. griffithianum* is gone, also *R. dalhousiae*, *R. maddeni*, *R. eximium*, *R. fulgens*, *R. hodgsonii*, and a dozen others once reported to be flowering in the garden are no longer here. *R. decorum* in Sikkim is in poor condition while Forrest's *R. griersonianum* plants are far from flourishing. Of the renowned blood-red *R. arboreum* there is now only one left, and that is just a fragment of what was once a much larger tree.

Old label for *R. campylocarpum* unearthed by a metal detector search during restoration

Many of the hybrids are doing better: they are not as old and their breeding guarantees them a degree of hardiness, but they too are beginning to go. Two great *R. arboreum x griffithianum* hybrids came down in 2006, one brought down by a huge weight of untimely April snow, and down the Western Ride you can see a 12 metre tree, now prostrate, felled by some autumn gale, the root ball torn out of the ground. The sight of this root ball gives a clue to their vulnerability. Rhododendrons are shallow rooted and as the protecting undergrowth of many years is removed, the roots can dry out and loosen their hold.

R. arboreum x griffithianum hybrid brought down by snow

It is not just age and accident that are taking their toll. There is another, more insidious, problem.

Several years ago there were rumours of a new disease that was causing widespread damage amongst the tan oaks of California. It was called Sudden Oak Death. The first isolated cases appeared in Cornwall in 2001 but the following years brought more cases of infection until, by the spring of 2004, *Phytophthora ramorum* was widespread in the county.

Little was known about this new disorder that had originated abroad, and sites that tested positive in the UK had every reason to fear: the method that was being used to control the spread of infection in North America was, quite literally, slash and burn. Whole areas of trees were being cleared and the infected plants incinerated.

Phytophthora ramorum is a fungal disease: the fruiting bodies release spores that are carried from one plant to another, spreading the infection. Water is an important vector and spores are carried by rain splash or in the warm moisture-laden air so characteristic of Cornwall. Spores are also spread when plants come into contact with each other or with people, carried on their hands, clothes and even shoes. The symptoms of the disease range from leaf necrosis and shoot die-back to bleeding cankers on the bark of mature trees.

In 2004, as the incidence of the disease increased, the situation was compounded by the emergence of another similar fungal infection, *Phytophthora kernoviae*. It quickly became clear that one of the most persistent hosts was the rhododendron and that amongst the other highly susceptible genera were both camellias and magnolias, together the three great flowering plants of Cornish gardens.

Heligan became infected and the future of its plants susceptible to these new diseases was under threat.

The future did indeed look bleak. It was unthinkable that these old plants could be lost but even worse to realize that if the plants themselves went, their unique genetic material would also be destroyed because vegetative propagation from infected plants was strictly forbidden. This would be an irreplaceable loss. There is genetic variation between plants of the same species and, within any set of seedlings, some are better specimens than others. Plants that have survived for an hundred and fifty years are likely to be good genetic selections.

Many of the old rhododendrons, however, are not species, they are hybrids; unnamed crosses, each different, each unique, each unrepeatable and this was the heritage that the new diseases were threatening to destroy.

In 2003 a Micropropagation Project was set up in conjunction with Duchy College, its purpose to propagate valuable and threatened plants. Heligan made a generous donation of £10,000 to buy the expensive equipment necessary for this work and, together with the Department for Environment, Food and Rural Affairs (Defra), has continued to support the Project. The key feature of this technique is that disease-free plants can be produced from infected material.

MICROPROPAGATION

In micropropagation small amounts of material are taken from the mother plant. This material, leaf or flower buds, is rigorously cleaned and placed in agar, a jelly containing nutrients and plant growth hormones to promote cell division.

The growth vessels are placed in the controlled atmosphere of the growth room where the optimum temperature of 23°C encourages the development of tiny shoots whilst light helps the correct orientation of the shoots. Leaves develop, each with a tiny axil bud at its base. These buds are excised, grown on to produce tiny shoots which develop leaves, each with a tiny axil bud at its base, and so on: the process is exponential, many new plants can be produced from a small piece of material.

When enough shoots have been generated, the agar formula is changed: auxins are added to encourage root growth and finally the tiny plants are potted up to be hardened off. The whole process takes about a year and what is of paramount importance is that new plants are free of infection.

Tiny shoots developing
from a flower bud.
Approx. size 1.5 cms

Growth Room where temperature, light and humidity are carefully controlled

More than half of the rhododendrons at Heligan have now been propagated and already young rhododendrons are being planted in the garden, including plants from the great red *R. arboreum* now dead on Flora's Green, the fragile *R. griersonianum* and *R. decorum*, the first of the micropropagated plants to flower.

The propagation of Heligan's rhododendrons is one part of the task of conserving them. *Phytophthora ramorum* and *Phytophthora kernoviae* are now endemic, so the emphasis must be on controlling the impact of these diseases rather than attempting to eradicate them.

Micropropagated *R. decorum*

R57 showing new growth a year after the initial drastic cutting back

The priority is to reduce the level of infection where it occurs. The most important control measure is the removal of all *R. ponticum*, the principal host plant of these diseases, and this has been done at Heligan. Where other rhododendrons have become infected but are considered too valuable to destroy, they are cut back to remove infected material, to prevent re-infection through rain splash from infected leaf litter and to avoid contact with other susceptible plants.

This pruning also helps to increase airflow through and around the plants, inhibiting the growth of the fungi, while a rigorous programme of clearing all potentially infected material from paths and borders helps to control the spread of disease. Raising the skirts of the rhododendrons on Flora's Green has had the added benefit of exposing the beauty of the structure of these great groups of plants.

The second part of the programme is to improve the cultural conditions of the plants, and this particularly applies to the young micropropagated plants, to encourage the healthy growth that will enable them to resist the diseases.